PLANTS AND FLOWERS
OF
SINGAPORE

PLANTS AND FLOWERS
OF
SINGAPORE

IVAN POLUNIN

TIMES EDITIONS

Frontispiece: *This Giant Mangrove Fern* (Acrostichum aureum) *illustrates the astonishing vigour and resilience of some of Singapore's vegetation. It grew from a microscopic spore in an abandoned coastal building site.*

© 1987 Times Editions Pte Ltd
Reprinted 1989, 1991, 1994

Times Editions Pte Ltd
Times Centre
1 New Industrial Road
Singapore 1953

Times Subang
Lot 46, Subang Hi-Tech Industrial Park
Batu Tiga
40000 Shah Alam
Selangor Darul Ehsan
Malaysia

Printed in Singapore.

ISBN 981 204 556 2

Contents

INTRODUCTION

There must be few people who open this page who do not know what a coconut palm or a banana plant look like. We all see vegetation every day of our lives and are utterly dependent on it. Yet I suspect that most of us ignore our green surroundings.

When I first came to South-east Asia from England 39 years ago, I found things so new and strange that they scarcely registered in my mind. This was certainly true of the plant life, which is some of the most luxuriant and diverse in the whole world. But gradually I learned to recognise more and more of the common plants and to know where and how they grew, and only then did they really begin to interest me.

Most people who live in Singapore are becoming ever more separated from the natural world, since 50 percent of the land area is built-up and a mere 14 percent is farm and woodlands, but with a little curiosity the plant kingdom can become a perennial source of pleasure and wonderment. People tend to take for granted what they see every day; I hope this book will kindle interest in the local plant life, as well as acting as an introduction and guide for visitors.

Although there are books on local ferns, mosses, wildflowers and seaweeds, I believe that this is the first which attempts a general account of higher plants and plant life in Singapore, excluding neighbouring countries. The extensive literature which is relevant to Singapore deals almost entirely with a wider area, the Malay Peninsula, most of which is currently known as Peninsular Malaysia, and only refers in passing to the small island at its southern tip.

More than four out of five Singaporeans live in high-rise apartments whose surrounding vegetation bears little relation to the vegetation of the original wilderness, or even to what is left of it in rural Singapore.

The visitor from outside the tropics will be confronted with a region whose plants are mostly

A wide range of vegetation is found on Bukit Timah Hill: dominating the top are the crowns of the trees of the original forest including (right of the coconut) the pale new leaves of a Seraya (Shorea curtisii). *The threat to this last surviving forest is shown by the group on the far right which have died for reasons unknown. Below the giants are the small trees of the* belukar, *with the fruit trees of a* kampung *lower down. In the foreground are young Macarthur's Palms.*

strange to him, and whose flowering plant species number perhaps 25,000, or about 10 percent of the world's total. Singapore probably has over 2,000 species. I say probably because, though the flora of the peninsula is fairly well known, we do not know which of these species are living in Singapore. This is partly because some of the species growing in Peninsular Malaysia do not reach south as far as Singapore. Although lists were published in 1900 by H.N. Ridley, then Director of the Singapore Botanic Gardens, and, for a majority of flowering plant families, by Associate Professor Hsuan Keng of the National University of Singapore in 1973–83, we do not know how many of these have become extinct here.

A book of this size can only describe perhaps ten percent of the species growing here, selected because they are beautiful, common, scientifically interesting or economically or historically important, and because adequate photographs are available. This may be frustrating, but the more demanding reader may take comfort in realising that he would have to wait decades for a comprehensive series of volumes, which would cost him a small fortune and bore him to tears, even if writers and a publisher could be found for it!

This book is aimed at those with no botanical knowledge. Most of the species illustrated should be recognisable with confidence from the photographs. I have avoided giving descriptive details of the plant as far as possible, especially of characteristics showing in the illustrations. Instead I have tried to tell "stories about plants", about their origin if they are not native to Singapore, their biology, and their place in people's lives.

For the serious student, for most plants illustrated in the section on species, I have given an abbreviated reference to an authoritative description in an up-to-date Flora. A Flora attempts to list and describe all the plants in the area covered. Unfortunately neither the Floras of Malaya, Thailand or Malesia (covering Malaysia, Singapore, Indonesia, Brunei and New Guinea) will be complete for several decades to come. This is because knowledge of this region's plants is limited and it has been said, with some truth, that while 90 percent of the world's botanists are in the temperate regions, 90 percent of the plant species are in the tropics.

I have used the scientific sys-

tem of naming plants because, unlike vernacular names, there is only one correct scientific name for each plant, though it may be extremely difficult to determine what it is. The first word of the scientific name is capitalised, and is a noun denoting the genus, a group consisting of one — or more usually a number of — similar species. The second word is an adjective, and denotes the species. Thus the Seashore Screwpine (p. 96) is *Pandanus odoratissimus*; *Pandanus* being the latinised form of the Malay name *pandan* while *odoratissimus* means "most scented".

Most tropical plants have been given several different names by different authors. A few of the old, and now unacceptable, names which still have wide currency are also given.

This book tries to answer the question, "How fares the plant kingdom on a small, humid, equatorial island largely covered by a burgeoning modern city?" I start by taking a brief look at the original vegetation of Singapore, and go on to describe the main types of man-modified vegetation in the countryside, and end by considering the largely new sorts of plant community which are the result of intensive human impact, and some of the exciting developments in the encouragement of plant life in Singapore.

Blooms are infrequent on the forest floor. Left: Labisia pumila *is a herb with leathery leaves.* Below: Kecubong Hutan (Randia macrophylla) *has lily-like flowers, but belongs to the Gardenia and Coffee family!*

Sundaland and present-day South-east Asia

LAOS

VIETNAM

THAILAND

KAMPUCHEA

N. boundary of Malesian flora

PHILIPPINES

Palawan

Songkhla
Alor Star

PENINSULAR
MALAYSIA

BRUNEI

EAST MALAYSIA

Wallace's line

SINGAPORE

Sumatra

Borneo

W. Ne
Guine

SUNDALAND

I N D O N E S I A

Celebes

Spice Islands

WALLACEA

Java

Bali

Wallace's line

S. and E. boundary of Malesian flor

AUSTRALIA

Key
Present-day SE Asia
Currently submerged
portions of Sundaland
(Sunda Shelf)

THE ORIGINAL SETTING

GEOGRAPHICAL LOCATION

Singapore lies 137 km. north of the equator and 104° east of Greenwich in an area largely surrounded by the shallow seas of the Sunda Shelf, the largest continental shelf in the world.

The map shows the 100-metre line which is the probable limit to which the coastline retreated during the last ice-age about 10,000 years ago. Singapore was then part of a huge landmass across which plants and animals could migrate. This landmass is called Sundaland, and it includes present-day mainland South-east Asia, the Malay Peninsula, the islands of Borneo, Sumatra, Java and Bali, Palawan in the Philippines and the shallow seas separating them. The rest of Indonesia and the Philippines was always separated from Sundaland by a deep water barrier.

Alfred Russel Wallace, the naturalist and pioneer zoogeographer, described the line between Sundaland and the islands

to the east, which is now called Wallace's Line. It marks the boundary between the fauna of Sundaland and that of the islands to the east, often called Wallacea by zoogeographers.

More recent studies suggest that the zoological boundary is not so abrupt, and that the fauna becomes progressively more Australian as the eastern end of the Lesser Sunda Islands is approached. Wallace's Line seems to be rather less important as a botanical boundary, perhaps because of the ability of vegetation to float, and of spores or seeds to survive hostile conditions. Some of these are blown by the winds or carried internally by fruit-eating birds and bats.

The most important botanical boundary near Singapore is a line running across the northern part of the Malay Peninsula, from a point near Alor Star in the north-west of Peninsular Malaysia, northward to reach the Gulf of Thailand near Songkhla. It appears to be largely a climatic boundary, with a marked dry season further north which is absent to the south. Around 500 genera of flowering plants occur on only one side of this line. Other more important botanical boundaries

A bio-geographical map of South-east Asia with present coastlines and those of Sundaland during the last ice age. It shows why similar species of plants are found in the region.

exist between Taiwan and the Philippines, and, most significant of all, between New Guinea and Australia. The land enclosed by these boundaries was called Malesia by Dr. C.G.G.J. van Steenis, the Dutch botanist who heads the important Flora Malesiana project.

Singapore Island now has a land area of 570 km²; including the other islands the total land area of the Republic is 618 km². Most of Singapore is covered by low hills, culminating in the granitic Bukit Timah Hill (162 m. above sea level), while to the western end there is a hilly area of sedimentary rocks, and extensive sand deposits are found at the eastern end.

Many of the lower hills in what are now housing and industrial estates have been levelled and the overburden used for land reclamation, which has recently increased the land area by nearly seven percent.

There were several estuaries on the northern and western coasts of the island supporting extensive mangroves. These have mainly been destroyed as the estuaries have been converted into freshwater reservoirs. In other areas large tracts of mangrove swamp have been filled and the land reclaimed for building. The largest surviving mangrove area is about four hectares at Pasir Ris.

THE CLIMATE

Singapore has a warm, humid climate with only slight seasonal variation. Mean daily temperature is 26·6°C with maximum of 30·7°C and minimum of 23·7°C. The highest and lowest shade temperatures ever recorded were 35·8°C and 19·6°C, so it is never very hot, nor is it cold. Variations between the mean monthly temperatures of different months are less than 1°C, so there is no cool season.

The main seasonal variation in Singapore is the rainy period from November to January. But this is only a season of slightly heavier rain, with an average of 25·5 cm. of rain per month, whereas in the driest month the average is nearly 17 cm., which is more than enough to allow rapid plant growth. Annual rainfall averages 2·37 metres and there is an average of nearly 200 rainy days a year.

Climate graph of Singapore showing monthly means of daily maximum (red line) and daily minimum (blue line) temperatures. The chart shows average monthly rainfall.

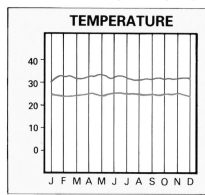

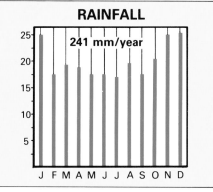

There is considerable variation in the rainfall from year to year, but even exceptional dry periods do little damage to most of the vegetation and tend to provoke flowering and fruiting of trees. As a result of this equable climate you can never tell the time of year by looking at the vegetation, as is possible in temperate regions.

The vegetation of Singapore shows the effect of this climate. It is lush green throughout the year. In general showy flowers are less evident than in temperate regions, though there are spectacular exceptions. It must be remembered that in the humid tropics flowering may be spread out through the year, even in species which have a definite flowering season in the monsoon tropics. Trees which drop their leaves during the dry season in the seasonal tropics, may remain leafy all the year round, or a leaf-fall may be followed immediately by new leaves. Trees like the Flame of the Forest (p. 128), which produces an annual blaze of colour during the dry season in the monsoon tropics, flower fitfully in Singapore. The climate encourages leafy growth, rather than blossom.

In spite of the equable climate, plants and animals do show seasonal rhythms. The most obvious and welcome of these is shown by the fruiting of durians, rambutans, mangosteens and some other fruits. This takes place around the middle and end of the year, though the fruiting is a response to dry weather conditions several months previously.

Some trees grow continuously and do not have a definite growing season. Some species have periods of growth alternating with periods of inactivity. These are synchronised in some species while in others the timing varies from tree to tree. In some tree species, like the mango (p. 144), different parts of the same tree may be at different stages of cycles of putting out new shoots and leaves, and of flowering and fruiting.

Weeds and pioneer species of tree tend to be free-flowering but with rather insignificant flowers. Many ornamental trees, of course, are specially selected for their frequent and showy flowering.

The distinctive crown of Albizia falcataria *is due to the even spacing out of its fine pinnate leaves and brittle branches. It can grow at an enormous rate and is very likely to sow itself at roadsides and in gardens. Unfortunately, it has a bad reputation for being easily uprooted. It produces mimosa-like flowers twice a year (p. 41).*

MAN'S INFLUENCE

Before modern Singapore was founded in 1819 there were only a few hundred inhabitants. There must have been some cleared ground around the settlement at the mouth of the Singapore River, where trees had been cut for temporary "slash and burn" cultivation, and for building houses and boats. It is also certain that there were fruit trees and other useful trees planted around homes and farmhouses.

Except for these, and for outlying clearings, the rest of the island was probably wilderness. The undulating land was covered with lowland evergreen forest. On flat land there was swamp forest down to the level of high water spring tides, when the freshwater swamp forest merged into mangrove. Where the shore was too rocky, sandy or exposed, the foreshore was bare, with beach forest only growing above the high tidemark.

Since 1819 there has been a continuous increase in population, except from 1942 to 1945. It reached 2,500,000 in 1983, and it is now increasing by 1·2 percent annually.

Important early crops were nutmegs (p. 152) and cloves, and gambier, a climbing shrub from whose leaves tannin was extracted. Today there are very few spice trees in Singapore outside the Botanic Gardens and gambier is only found in the Catchment Area, where it grows wild.

Contrary to popular belief, soils in Singapore are generally poor, it is the warmth and moisture which encourage rapid plant growth. Undulating areas have rapid chemical weathering of bedrock, producing a layer of clayey subsoil which may be many metres deep. Unfortunately most of the available plant nutrients liberated by weathering are washed out of the subsoil by heavy rains, while the rich supply of nutrients liberated by the weathering of bedrock is too deep down to be available to plants. Large areas of hilly land which were planted with gambier and tapioca (p. 37) in the earlier days were abandoned after several years of cultivation, and have been permanently degraded. Some of these remain as scrubland as on Pasir Panjang Ridge.

This five-foot-way "garden" was photographed in Chinatown. The plants in the dragon pots are, from left to right, ginger (Zingiber officinale), pomegranate (Punica granatum), a jasmine, and a young mango tree!

15

Singapore soils are more suited to the cultivation of tree crops, which are less demanding and provide some protection against soil washout. In the second decade of this century, rubber became the principal tree crop. Although they are no longer tapped, extensive rubber plantations still remain at the time of writing, such as those on the east side of Woodlands Road between the 19th and 20th km. stones. Coconut (p. 154) was another important crop, and extensive plantations can be found on the east side of the island.

HOMES AND GARDENS

In the past Chinese urban settlement was distinct from other types and involved the building of shophouses with a five-foot way. This left no space for trees lining the road, and there was usually not enough space between rows of houses to allow for gardens. So plant life was rather restricted and similar to that still found in long-established Chinatown areas.

Other forms of settlement were more open. The houses of wealthier merchants and government officials had spacious gardens, and sometimes plantations, while those of Chinese farmers and Malay *kampung* dwellers were usually scattered, with fruit trees planted around the house and often a small plantation or farm

A bamboo in flower. There are many species of bamboo in Singapore. The stems are very useful and the young shoots of some species are cooked as a vegetable.

attached. As the pressure on land became greater, gardens declined in size, and farms became smaller and more intensively cultivated.

The main response to the increased population density in the last 20 years has been to live in high-rise apartments. By 1984, over 77 percent of the population were living in apartments built by the Housing and Development Board, which are nearly all high-rise, and the proportion continues to increase. Besides this, there are private apartments and condominiums. Most apartment blocks only occupy a small proportion of the land, and the remaining ground not occupied by car parks is planted with mainly introduced species of trees, forming a sort of grassy parkland.

FAMOUS BOTANISTS

In the early days Singapore was the centre for botanical investigations of what is now Peninsular Malaysia, during a period of intense interest in the exploration and exploitation of the plant kingdom. Sir Thomas Stamford Raffles, the founder of modern Singapore, had an experimental plantation of nutmeg and clove trees laid out on Government Hill, and his association with the physician and botanist Dr. Joseph Arnold is commemorated in the naming of the largest flower in the world, *Rafflesia arnoldi*, which they found while travelling together in Sumatra.

The present Singapore Botanic Gardens dates from 1860 and was started by the Agri-Horticultural Society, but was taken over by the government in 1874 because of its debts. An Economic Garden was opened in 1879 on a site later occupied by Raffles College, where university studies in botany first began in buildings which are now part of the Institute of Education. Part of this land, a strip along Cluny Road which stretches as far as Bukit Timah Road, has recently been developed as an extension to the Botanic Gardens, to which it is connected by a passageway under Cluny Road.

The Gardens started as a pleasure park for wealthy Society members and then became a centre for trying out economic plants. With the appointment of Ridley, the first botanist to be Director, the Gardens became a centre of botanical research. Ridley was Director from 1888 to 1912 and undertook extensive botanical explorations in Singapore, the Malay Peninsula and Indonesia, discovering, describing and naming hundreds of previously unknown species. This work came to fruition after his retirement, when his five-volume *Flora of the Malay Peninsula* was published between 1922 and 1925. It was a great achievement in its day, but is now considerably outdated.

He is, however, best known as the "father" of the plantation rubber industry. Para Rubber trees (*Hevea brasiliensis*) were growing in the Gardens when he arrived, but seemed to have no prospects because latex was extracted by slashing the trees, severely damaging them. Ridley refined a method which had already been used in Ceylon and found that it was possible to extract latex for an unlimited period, without significantly weakening the tree, by making a diagonal cut in the bark down to the layer of the latex canals. On alternate days the canals were reopened by removing a thin sliver of bark from the lower side of the cut, after which the latex oozed out and flowed along the cut, to be collected in a cup. The story goes that he had considerable difficulty in persuading planters to try growing Para Rubber, and that his persistence earned him the title of "Mad" Ridley.

I.H. Burkill was Director for the next 23 years and is famous for his encyclopaedic *Dictionary of the Economic Products of the Malay Peninsula*, published in 1935, which described the uses to which the products, mainly of vegetable origin, were put. His son, H.M. Burkill, who was Director from 1957–69 is still working

Tapping the Para Rubber tree using the method developed in Singapore nearly 100 years ago by H.N. Ridley.

at the Royal Botanic Gardens, Kew, on a second edition of his father's book.

Other distinguished botanists who worked in Singapore were Dr. R.E. Holttum and Prof. E.J.H. Corner. Holttum was the Gardens' Director from 1926 to 1949, after which he became the first Professor of Botany at the University of Malaya, the forerunner of the present National University of Singapore. He produced the first two volumes of *A Revised Flora of Malaya*, on orchids and ferns, a speciality of his.

Holttum played an important role in starting the orchid industry in Singapore when he introduced recently-discovered methods for growing them from seed. Orchid seeds sown in the ordinary way only develop occasionally. This is because they are minute and the seedlings cannot manufacture their own sugar; this has to be done for them by fungi which live inside the cells of the plant. So the seeds are cultivated on sterilised culture media such as *agar-agar*, to which has been added the necessary mineral salts and sugar. It was now possible to grow hybrid seeds and to produce a vast number of different orchids of which a very few have turned out to be ideally suited for the export cut flowers industry. There is now a permanent display of these methods in the Orchid Enclosure of the Botanic Gardens and research on orchid culture is still a main concern of the Gardens.

Now in his 90th year, Dr. Holttum continues his researches on ferns, on which he is the most distinguished authority. It is worth noting that Ridley and his plant collector Ahmad bin Hassan reached the age of 100 and I.H.

Burkill lived to 94 years. Health-conscious readers may note that the study and love of plants seems to promote a long and happy life!

E.J.H. Corner was Assistant Director from 1929–42. He is one of the few botanists whose scientific writings are refreshingly lively and imaginative. He is best known for his works on fungi, the natural history of palms, flower structure, and Malayan trees, among other subjects.

Corner used the "first apes to enter Government Service", pigtail monkeys (berok, *Macaca nemestrina*), which are trained by Malays to pick coconuts. He used them to collect botanical specimens from the treetops. This explains the curious rhyme on the endpaper of Volume Two of his *Wayside Trees of Malaya* (1940):

"Malayan Trees Who Cares to Know
Upon his shoulders sits a *Berok*".

Corner is Emeritus Professor of Tropical Botany at Cambridge University.

Nowadays the Department of Botany at the National University of Singapore is the principal centre of botanical learning in the Republic.

Two of the steps involved in the creation of a hybrid orchid. Left: Removing the pollen masses (on pencil tip) from an orchid. Orchids have specialised pollen masses with sticky bases which attach to the heads of pollinating insects. The pollen is then transferred to the stigma of another orchid. Right: The tiny hybrid seeds are cultivated in a special nutrient medium under sterile conditions. The seedlings in the right-hand flask are ready to be transplanted.

THE ORIGINAL VEGETATION

MARINE PLANTS

In the lower part of the inter-tidal zone are found seaweeds and a few species of flowering plants, loosely called sea grasses. They do not penetrate far below the low tidemark because they are dependent on sunlight.

The seaweeds or macroscopic marine algae are smaller and produce a much sparser growth than is found on coasts in the temperate regions. The only large seaweeds, over a metre long, belong to the genus *Sargassum*. It is not clear why this should be so. The apparent nutritional poverty of tropical seas compared with temperate seas is a possible explanation. However, the seas around Singapore and in the Straits of Malacca are not so poor in nutrient minerals, as they receive the discharge of waters of nutrient-rich rivers.

Seaweeds need hard surfaces on which to anchor, and so are attached to rocks or corals, to stones lying on sand or mud. About 200 species are described in Teo and Wee's book on Singapore seaweeds.

By contrast, the sea grasses are more prolific in Singapore and

Left: *The last remnant of the great forest which covered Singapore, the Bukit Timah Nature Reserve contains a great diversity of tree species and lianas. The fissured red-brown bark of the tree in the centre shows it is a* Seraya (Shorea curtisii).

Right: *The brown seaweed (Padina sp.) and the green seaweed (Halimeda sp.) can be seen at low tide on sandy coral flats.*

neighbouring coasts than in temperate climates. The five species in Singapore, which make up more than ten percent of the known species of sea grasses in the world, belong to the Frogbit family, but none are true grasses. They usually grow on sandy coral flats, though *Enhalus*, the Giant Seagrass (p. 64), also grows on muddy shores. They are anchored to the soft bottom by their un-branched roots, and are the favourite food of marine turtles. They survive mainly in the southern islands.

MANGROVE

Mangrove is a type of forest almost confined to the tropical regions, and consists of a few species of trees, shrubs and herbs

which tolerate and sometimes even require salt or brackish water, and which occupy the upper parts of the intertidal zone. In the mangrove forests of the whole world, there are only about 50 tree species and nearly half of these occur in the region, and are probably surviving in Singapore.

Mangrove can grow wherever there is a muddy foreshore which is sufficiently undisturbed by wave action or by human interference. It may grow to a lesser extent on sandy and stony shores.

Most flowering plants have seeds, which are the resting and dispersal phase of the plant. The situation is rather different for most of the tree species of the mangrove where development continues past the seed stage to produce a green plantlet which has a well developed rudimentary root and shoot. When such a plantlet becomes detached from the tree it falls, and as it floats and can stay alive for months, it may travel long distances before being washed ashore and taking root.

Mangrove trees have specialised roots which allow them to live in the mud. These may be stilt roots, knee roots, ribbon-shaped roots or tower roots which may be pencil-shaped or broad-based and tapering. Part of each such root is always sticking out of the mud, exposed to the air at low tide. The exposed parts are richly supplied with air pores, which normally appear as light brown raised patches of loose corky cells. They are waterproof at high tide when they are inundated, but at low tide they absorb air which can pass along the roots through air channels. This is important because mangrove mud below the surface may be devoid of oxygen.

These roots have another less obvious function. The delicate feeding roots, through which water and dissolved nutrients are absorbed, can only survive in the oxygen-containing surface layers of the soil. If more mud is deposited, as is the usual situation in mangrove, new feeding roots can be produced from the breathing roots, just below the surface of the mud.

Some species, which include *Avicennia* trees and the thorny herb *Acanthus* (p. 64), excrete salt by means of special glands on the leaves. The roots of some mangrove trees have the ability to absorb fluid containing a lower concentration of salt than that present outside the plant. Old leaves of certain species thicken and contain tissues with a high concentration of salt, which may

be a way of getting rid of the excess salt. It seems that these are some of the characteristics which allow mangrove trees to survive in a salty environment.

BEACH VEGETATION

Mangrove merges into swamp forest above the high water spring tide level, whenever the gradient is gentle enough, but all such places in Singapore have been greatly disturbed. Wherever mangrove forest cannot grow, the upper part of the foreshore is bare

Far left: *At high tide the mangrove provides food and shelter for marine life. The high prop roots are characteristic of* Rhizophora apiculata.

Below: *Mangroves (*R. mucronata) *form a thin line on the poor soil of a coral foreshore.*

of vegetation up to the extreme high tidemark.

Where the shore is sandy, and especially where new land is being formed, the beach is colonised by a small number of plants, of which the most obvious are the creeping Sea Morning Glory (p. 66), certain sedges and the sea beans, *Canavalia maritima* with pink flowers (p. 66) and *Vigna marina* with yellow flowers. Some of these plants have creeping rootstocks and help to stabilise the shore.

The Casuarina, looking like a feathery fir-tree, is a hardy colonist of newly-deposited sand just above the high tidemark. On the east coast of Peninsular Malaysia it forms a narrow, continuous strip of trees in suitable places. On the reclaimed beaches of Changi it is sowing itself freely from trees which have been planted, while Sea Lettuce (p. 96), growing on the edge of the seashore, has sown itself from floating seeds.

There was a characteristic coastal strand forest but it has been almost completely destroyed in Singapore, though patches of it can be seen on the Sister Islands and at Labrador Park. This strand forest contains only a small number of tree species, which suggests that it is a difficult environment to colonise.

Many of the trees and herbs of the beach have a wide natural geographical distribution, from the shores of East Africa to the central Pacific Ocean or even round the globe. This is probably due to the ability of the fruits to float, and for the seeds to be able to germinate after many months at sea. Such a seed can travel for thousands of kilometres before sprouting on a distant shore.

FRESHWATER SWAMP FOREST

Originally there was extensive swamp forest in Singapore, in the lower reaches of the Singapore and Kallang rivers. A large area was felled in 1940, and is now under Seletar Reservoir. The only swamp forest left is the lower part of this downstream from Seletar Reservoir dam. The gradient in swamp forest is so low, and the obstructions to the flow of water caused by clumps of roots are so great that in rainy weather, swamp forest can be a sheet of slowly moving water for weeks on end.

Though some species of tree typical of well-drained lowland forest are able to live in this watery habitat, most of the tree species are only found in swamp

forest. Some of them have breathing roots similar to those of mangrove species. Thus there are stilt roots, knee roots, tower roots and peg roots. Generally speaking the trees are shorter and the forest structure less complex than in the next type of forest.

LOWLAND EVERGREEN FOREST

This, the so-called tropical rain forest, originally covered most of the island. Now it is confined to the Bukit Timah Nature Reserve, an area of 75 hectares, which includes and is named after Singapore's highest hill. It is easily accessible from Upper Bukit Timah Road at Ewart Circus, which is about 12 km. from the GPO. It is then only a walk of about 450 m. up Hindhede Drive to the start of the Reserve. But even here there has been some disturbance. There is a road to the top (which is closed to public vehicles), and an extensive system of well-maintained footpaths. Taban Valley, near the entrance, on the right-hand side, is the site of an old plantation of gutta percha or *Taban* (*Palaquium gutta*). These trees can be recognised by the diagonal slash marks where the bark was cut to make the latex flow.

Sights from Singapore's surviving swamp forest. Left: Rooted in the mud is Cryptocoryne griffithii, *while the roots of a woody plant trail in the clear waters of a sluggish stream. Below:* The knee-shaped breathing root of a swamp forest tree richly supplied with yellow, corky lenticels helps the tree to survive in the poorly-oxygenated, peaty soil.

There is also some concern about the future of this forest. It is so small that it is influenced by the warming and drying of Singapore due to urbanisation, while quarrying and felling have increasingly exposed the trees to winds leading to more treefalls. Whatever damage may have occurred, the forest is still magnificent and merits a visit.

There is also a four-hectare area of primary forest, the Botanic Gardens' Jungle. Unfortunately many of the older trees in certain parts have gone, and Professor Corner told me that he thought that this might be the delayed result of damage from shellfire during World War Two. Some of the gaps have been occupied by quick-growing opportunist trees. Besides this, there has been serious overgrowth of some trees by creepers and some interference with the original ground cover by planting the very poisonous, large-leaved, alien ornamental herb *Dieffenbachia.*

Tropical rain forest is the most complex eco-system known to exist, and it reaches its greatest complexity in South-east Asia. It is the "climax" vegetation which ultimately develops in those parts of the tropics where there is a high rainfall evenly distributed throughout the year, with no severe dry season. Such forest occurs in three main blocks, in tropical America, Asia and Africa, and the forest in these different continents shows a general similarity.

However, the species in the three areas are all different, and so are most of the genera to which these belong. This is because the main regions of this type of forest have been separated by water barriers for so long that evolution has taken place independently in each region. The general similarities are an example of convergent evolution — species in different continents evolving under similar conditions, and developing similar characteristics which enhance their biological fitness under those conditions.

One of the most obvious characteristics of rain forest is the large number of species. This is best illustrated by the trees, but it is also true for many groups of animals. A temperate forest is likely to contain about 10 species of tree, with one species dominant, as in oak, fir or pine forest. The forest in Bukit Timah contains hundreds of tree species, so that any one species is likely to be represented by single individuals, widely separated from other trees of the same species, or even by the sole representative of that species in Singapore.

The reasons for this great diversity are not at all clear. One obvious cause could be the age of the habitat, as evolution takes very long periods of time, especially in trees where the interval between generations may be several decades. It would seem that the present-day flora of the rain forest has descended from plants which lived in warm, humid conditions without major climatic disturbances from the times when flowering plants first appeared over 100 million years ago. This contrasts with the situation in cool, temperate areas where the ice came and went in a series of ice ages, each obliterating plant life over wide areas.

A generally favourable environment which does not require extreme adaptations to extreme conditions appears to encourage species diversity, and rain forest is such an environment. By contrast we can note the small number of species in mangrove and beach forest, which are generally considered to be very unfavourable environments.

Where physical conditions encourage growth, interactions between living organisms become more important, and with so many species involved the complexity becomes enormous. It has been suggested that each species has its own ecological niche, or way of life. From this point of view, the forest environment is seen as a multi-mosaic of different micro-environments, with each tree making its own micro-environment. This is true once the tree is big enough to capture enough light for rapid growth and to shade the vegetation below it, but all trees started out as small seedlings with insignificant effects on the environment. The seedling that survived to become a forest giant did not do so just because of an innate greater ability to survive in a unique environment. Other factors and chance itself must have played a part.

It used to be thought that ecosystem complexity led to stability. Major change is more likely if a single species is dominant, when it may be damaged by a single predator or parasite reaching plague proportions. The rain forest under natural conditions has been very stable for

The striking orange pods and black seeds of Sterculia coccinea, *a forest treelet, add a flash of colour to the darkness of the forest. Its leaves and those of the Fishtail Palm below support a growth of lichens.*

many millions of years and can withstand windstorms and lightning strikes. But it is extremely vulnerable to greater disturbances, such as logging, and forest species with highly specialised requirements may be replaced, more or less permanently, by more adaptable species, often from outside.

Soils of even the richest humid tropical forests may be poor sources of the scarce mineral nutrients needed for plant growth. On the surface is the leaf litter, which falls throughout the year. It rots quickly in the warm, moist conditions of the forest. Most of the available nutrients are in the

Many forest trees have hanging leaves with pointed tips. These "drip tips" may speed up the drying of leaves.

vegetation, both living and dead, and so absorption of nutrients by trees takes place largely in the deeper layers of the leaf litter and in the thin, humus-rich top layer of the soil, often only millimetres thick in some places, and completely absent in others.

Nearly all the root system is in the topmost 0·3 m. of the soil, the zone richest in nutrients and oxygen, and a mass of roots can often be seen growing upwards from the surface of the soil into the deeper layers of partially decomposed leaf litter. The forest, by the rapid recycling of nutrients, is able to maintain a massive biomass with a high rate of turnover on poor soils. This recycling is due to the activities of many different kinds of fungi, bacteria, termites and other small invertebrate animals.

FOREST LAYERS

There is a great range in height of different plant species in the forest, which we can think of as consisting of five layers, provided we realise that these layers merge imperceptibly into each other, and are usually discontinuous. Starting from above are the emergent trees, over 50 m. high, consisting of individual trees or groups towering over the others.

Only certain species are able to achieve emergent status and many of these are Dipterocarps. Near the Hampstead Hut of the Bukit Timah Nature Reserve, a series of *Seraya* trees form an almost pure stand on the ridge. It is unusual to find an area of rain forest heavily dominated by one species, though this is typical of *Seraya*.

Below the emergents is the main canopy, which tends to be continuous, except where shaded by emergents or where a tree has fallen. Under this a third layer consists of trees shaded by the canopy, and generally having narrow spindly trunks, branching as they grow up. The fourth and fifth layers consist of treelets, and herbaceous plants together with small tree seedlings.

The micro-climate changes dramatically from canopy to ground level. Above is full sunlight, with the greatest variation in temperature and humidity; while at ground level only about two percent of the sunlight penetrates, the temperature is cool and varies little, and the forest floor may stay moist for days after rain.

Such a static scheme of forest layers may make us lose sight of the fact that the tallest emergent grew from a seed, through the different layers.

Another way of thinking about the forest is as a mosaic of gaps left by treefalls. These gaps are of different ages. Recent gaps, perhaps 10 percent of the forest area, are occupied by trees that are still growing rapidly upwards. Still older gaps are filled by more or less mature trees.

Young trees tend to be tall and spindly, with widely scattered branches producing a narrow crown. Mature forest trees of the larger species tend to end up with a tall, relatively slender, straight and unbranching cylindrical trunk which only tapers significantly near the top, where a number of branches support an umbrella-shaped crown. However, the shape of a tree is determined both by genetic endowment and by its environment. The leaves are most often medium-sized and leathery. The bark is usually thin, smooth and pale in colour.

TYPICAL RAIN FOREST PLANT TYPES

Buttressed trees

Many forest trees have prominent buttresses, and the trunk tapers as the ground is approached. This would appear to be a response to tension in the trunk and roots, as buttresses are better developed on the uphill side of slopes. They may play a part in preventing the tree from being blown down, although they are not always successful in this. Treefall probably occurs because the root system of rain forest trees is shallow though some species have also developed deep roots.

Cauliflorous plants

Flower heads which issue from trunks or major branches are common in trees and climbers of the humid tropics but rare in temperate climates. They are found in durians (p. 142), *Artocarpus* and some figs (p. 120). It is not clear what benefit, if any, is enjoyed by this type of tree, but it cannot be an accident.

The amount of wood which must be produced to lift the leaves of a forest tree to the canopy is enormous. It is therefore not surprising that plants have evolved several strategies to gain exposure to light, using the support provided by trees.

Climbers

Climbers are plentiful and important in the forest. Some species reach a great height such as the Bauhinias, which climb by means of tendrils, and the flexible Rattan Palms (p. 40), which use hooks to scramble upward. Besides these there are large woody twiners such as *Gnetum*. Climbers have thin, flexible stems which act like cables and have a higher proportion of sap-containing tubes and a lower proportion of fibres in their stems than the trees which support them. They take a share of the sunlight but in some areas, when the forest is logged, they may produce such a thick overgrowth as to interfere seriously with forest regeneration. Some others climb by attachments to the tree trunk by means of roots, such as *Freycinetia* of the Screwpine family, and various Aroids, some of which also send down roots to ground level to absorb nutrients.

Epiphytes

Epiphytes are plants which grow on other plants. Most of these are virtually harmless to the trees except on the mountain tops of neighbouring countries where the epiphytes in moss forests can crowd out leaves on the branches. However, in Singapore the little creeping fern *Drymoglossum piloselloides* may crowd out leaves on smaller branches. On the leathery, long-lived leaves of some forest plants there may be a thick growth of microepiphytes such as algae, mosses and liverworts. Epiphytes must survive desiccation and some of them have succulent leaves like those of desert plants.

Parasites

Members of the Mistletoe family are semi-parasites. They are usually attached to the smaller branches of trees by special roots which penetrate the host's wood and absorb water, salts and some sugars, although their green leaves and stems are able to produce their own sugars by photosynthesis. They have a harmful effect on the trees they parasitise and some species are common in Singapore.

Things seen in the forest. Above: The tough leathery leaves of some shrubs last several years and may become covered with micro-epiphytes, lichens, algae and even mosses.
Left: *The spiny stem of a climbing rattan palm* (Daemonorops didymophylla) *bears a load of scaly fruit. These are covered with a red encrusting resin, called "dragon's blood", used as a dye and in traditional medicine.*
Right: *Many kinds of fungi grow on dead tree trunks. The white one is a species of bracket fungus, the orange one is* Gymnopilus dilepis.

Stranglers

Strangling figs have an extraordinary life history. The small seeds are often deposited on trees after passing through the guts of birds or bats which have swallowed the figs, and they start life as epiphytes. They then let down thin flexible roots which enter the ground. These thicken and become stout woody tree trunks, and may damage or kill the tree by shading it.

In other species, roots grow over the tree trunk and, making contact with each other, become grafted together to form a woody basketwork. It is usually assumed that basket figs strangle their supporting trees, but this may not be so as these figs do not cut into the growing support tree, as do some stout woody twiners. However, we need observations and experiments to determine whether figs really strangle trees, or just shade them.

TRANSIENT HABITATS

The plant species which grow in open and disturbed habitats in Singapore, with very few exceptions, are unable to grow in tropical rain forest. Where were all these plants when Singapore was virtually covered with forest?

A partial answer is that many of the common weeds of open ground were not here. This includes the very aggressive climber Mile a Minute (*Lupang, Mikania micrantha*), the three species of *Mimosa, Lantana* (p. 98) and the ubiquitous Carpet Grass (*Axonopus compressus*), all of which are natives of tropical America. But many of the herbs, and some of the trees, were true natives which probably survived in transient habitats where the earth was exposed for a limited period of time, allowing sun-loving species to grow, provided the seeds could get there in the first place.

When a big forest tree falls, its crown clears a considerable area. Sometimes other trees can be knocked down as it falls, an event which is sometimes specially-arranged by tribal peoples when they clear the forest for their shifting cultivation. Treefall, which usually involves the uprooting of shallow-rooted trees, also effects a sort of crude tillage, allowing the establishment of seedlings that would be unlikely to grow in deep leaf litter.

Landslides are another means by which the ground is denuded. They were probably rare in Singapore before human settlement, but there have been extensive landslides on Bukit Timah Hill after exceptional rainfall. Other transient sites are exposed by the action of rivers. On the outside bends erosion of the bank may occur, exposing the bare earth, while on the inside bends deposits of silt after floods may become dry enough to support transient plant life.

Forest floor with a fruit and dead leaf of Dipterocarpus grandiflorus. *Between the fallen leaves can be seen decomposing leaf litter, which is rich in nutrients and has many tree rootlets growing into it.*

AGRICULTURAL ACTIVITY AND ITS EFFECT ON VEGETATION

The great forest of Singapore was cleared many years ago, but forest felling is still continuing at speed in all neighbouring countries. Trees were clear-felled and left to lie on the ground for a month or more. Then, preferably on a hot and windy afternoon with the brushwood tinder-dry after several rainless days, it was set alight. If the burn was poor, the remaining brushwood might be gathered together and fired again. The soil, covered with ash which is rich in potash and phosphorus, was planted with crops as soon as possible after burning.

HERBACEOUS CROPS

Various herbaceous crops were grown, even when the land was planted up with a tree crop. These included pulses and cereals.

Tapioca (p. 37) was always an important crop, and was grown both as a source of food and of

An aerial view of farmland in Singapore showing the patchwork of intensively cultivated plots. The raised beds of green leafy vegetables and vines, possibly cucumbers, are typical, as are the coconut palms, banana plants and other fruit trees around the zinc-roofed farmhouses. In the foreground is some belukar, while there are fishponds in the background.

starch. It is a poor source of human nutrients, containing mainly starch and a low concentration of protein of unusually poor biological value. It is regarded as a food for hard times; it is easy to grow, heavy yielding and it can be stored in the soil. The young leaves can also be eaten. Tapioca had a reputation for being particularly liable to exhaust the soil but this was probably due to the practice of growing several crops of it in succession.

When the land was finally abandoned, it often reverted to lallang grass (p. 78), which could persist for long periods because of its resistance to fire.

Early crops include leafy, fruiting and root vegetables. Gambier (*Uncaria gambir*) is a woody vine which climbs by means of hooks, and the old leaves were harvested for 15 years or more, after which the land was usually abandoned. Pepper (*Piper nigrum*) was also grown in early Singapore. It is a perennial root climber and is usually grown on posts.

These early crops were grown by methods which exhausted the fertility of the soil after a few years. When the supply of land ran out, their cultivation moved to neighbouring countries.

Pineapples (p. 142) became an important crop in Singapore nearly 100 years ago, when a canning factory was opened, but cultivation soon moved to Johor. The pineapple plant is still a common survivor in overgrown places which are the sites of old plantations, but it does not produce fruit under these conditions. Tapioca can also survive for many years in old plantings.

Giant fruit-producing herbs, like bananas and papayas (p. 144), are common in gardens, and these plants are still cultivated commercially.

Singapore soils are not rich enough to allow continuous cultivation of herbaceous crops without the heavy addition of fertilisers, while on sloping land there is serious erosion due to torrential rainstorms.

Land is now so scarce and valuable that commercial cultivation is only economical for crops of high value. Vegetables are still grown, but less extensively than in the Thirties, when there were estimated to be 1,200 hectares of market gardens. Vegetable gardening has mainly been undertaken by Chinese, using traditional methods. The crops were grown on raised beds, and the farmer often also raised pigs (which are now banned on small-holdings) and various sorts of carp in fishponds. Leafy vegetables, and vegetables which are technically fruits, were grown by extremely intensive methods often involving the labour of the whole family.

On flat alluvial land in the Kallang River basin, on either side of Braddell Road, there used to be what was perhaps the most labour-intensive and productive market gardening in the world.

Up to eight crops were produced a year, with hand tilling of the vegetable beds, a liberal application of prawn dust as fertiliser, and watering up to twice daily during dry weather from watering cans carried on yokes. Seedlings were transplanted by hand, and shaded from the sun for the next few days.

The vegetables produced were Amaranth Spinach (*Bayam, Amaranthus gangeticus*), dry land *kangkong* (p. 150), watercress (*Nasturtium officinale*), mustard greens (*choy sum,* p. 150) and Chinese kale (*kai-lan, Brassica alboglabra*). Besides these, floating water plants such as Water Hyacinth (p. 68) and Water Lettuce (*Kiambang, Pistia stratiotes*) were grown in shallow ponds for pig-food.

Vegetables are still being grown on undulating land, especially in the Mandai and Sembawang areas. They include long beans (p. 148), several members of the cucumber family, and eggplants (p. 148). They are nowadays watered by pump and hose from a sump pond or well which receives back the water and dissolved fertiliser when it drains from the land. Sweet potatoes (*Ipomoea batatas*) and tapioca do not need such special attention.

New types of commercial cultivation have recently been developed. Orchid growing for the cut-flower export trade is now an important small industry, with an export value of S$15 million in 1979. These orchids are free-flowering hybrids whose ancestors were epiphytic species, and they are planted in a mixture of broken bricks and charcoal beds, or in pots, and are watered by dilute solutions of fertiliser applied to the leaves.

There are also farms devoted to

the cultivation of aquatic plants which are exported to temperate countries for tropical aquarium enthusiasts.

Pioneering work on the cultivation of edible mushrooms has been undertaken by the Primary Production Department, and by commercial growers. There is a lack of traditional materials in Singapore for growing mushrooms; no horse manure for the Common Mushroom, and no padi straw for the Padi Straw Mushroom. However, those are now being grown successfully here, using readily available materials, such as cotton waste, sawdust and old newspapers. Even the "black" Shiitake Mushroom, which had to be grown on oakwood, is now cultivated in Singapore.

It is possible to buy ready-to-grow blocks of cotton waste, impregnated with appropriate nutrients and mushroom spawn, and covered in plastic. When watered and kept in a cool, dark place they give a heavy yield of delicious mushrooms for many weeks. Home mushroom growing could be a very satisfying hobby which does not need a garden — only cupboard space.

'Fungi are beautiful, and the aesthetic side of fungus cultivation is almost unexplored territory. There are several species of luminous toadstools in the forest. I look forward to the day when I receive an invitation, my host dims the lights and opens the cupboard, and lo and behold, a glowing garden of green-gold or blue luminous toadstools!

Nursery gardens for ornamental plants were plentiful along roadsides, and their beautiful display of flowering and foliage plants in pots is surely the most welcome kind of advertising. Most of the nurserymen have had to move from their original sites, though a few remain. A group of nurseries have recently been established on the west side of Thomson Road at 7 km.

TREE CROPS

Tree crops are more suited to Singapore conditions than are herbaceous crops, and they allow the land to be permanently cultivated without serious deterioration. Useful trees, especially fruit

Tapioca (Ubi kayu, Manihot esculenta) *is a large herb which grows freely from pieces of stem stuck in the ground. The tuber contains starch, but the outer part must be discarded to avoid poisoning from hydrocyanic acid.*

trees, were planted around houses from the earliest times, together with herbaceous food plants. Tree crops were usually planted soon after the felled forest or scrub had been cleared by burning, and were inter-planted with non-woody crops, which were mostly phased out when there was too much shade for them to thrive.

Nutmeg (p. 152) and clove (*Eugenia caryophylla*) trees were grown in early Singapore, and later on coffee, but these are now rarely found.

Coconuts (p. 154) have always been planted around houses, as

The edge of an abandoned rubber estate in February or March, as can be seen from the 'autumn' colours of the leaves on the rubber trees. On the right there is a patch of tree ferns (Cyathea sp.).

they probably have more uses than any other plant. Furthermore they are hardy, only requiring a well-drained soil, and thus are often planted on the poorer, sandy soils of the eastern part of Singapore. Frequently coconut plantations were on hilly ground, but they have been planted down to the level of the highest tides. Coconut palms, with their high crowns, let through much sunlight, so there is usually a considerable ground cover of grasses and other herbaceous plants growing under them.

However, the surviving coconut plantations are now in a state of serious decline, as most areas where they grow are scheduled for development and will soon disappear. Many of the trees are dying, and this is probably because good hygienic practices

have ceased. Thus trees are allowed to rot, providing suitable conditions for the larvae of the Giant Red Striped Palm Weevil (*Rhynchophorus*). One of these beetles can eat the single growing point of the tree and kill it.

The coconut is one of the most useful plants in the world. As a domestic plant, its main uses are for coconut milk, which is the base for Malay curries, as the source of coconut water from the unripe fruit, and as a flavouring for cakes and sweetmeats.

The sap exuding from the bruised, freshly-cut end of the young flower-shoot is rich in sugar. It was formerly collected and left to ferment to produce *toddy*, the favourite alcoholic drink of Indian labourers, in the old days when *toddy* shops were run by the government. Alternately the excess water would be boiled off. On cooling, the sugar crystallised producing the delicious dark-brown *gula Melaka*.

When grown on a large scale the principal product of coconuts is copra, the dried flesh of the ripe fruit from which coconut oil is pressed, leaving behind a protein-rich animal feed. The shell produces the highest grade of charcoal, and the husk can be made into matting.

Rubber was first planted on a large scale in Singapore in the first decade of this century, and reached its peak between the two World Wars; since then there has been little cultivation.

The trees are planted in rows, and the shade is often so deep that there is little or no vegetation on the ground, even though there has been no weeding for many years. Most of Singapore's remaining rubber is old seedling rubber, easily distinguishable at a glance as the trunk tapers rapidly from the ground upwards. In the more modern plantations, however, the trees are bud-grafted, using buds from high-yielding clones. Bud-grafted trees can be distinguished by their very uniform appearance and cylindrical trunks.

ABANDONED CULTIVATED LAND

When cultivation ceases the ground rapidly becomes covered with grasses, and the somewhat similar sedges (*Cyperaceae*) and other herbaceous weeds. The quickest to be established are what are usually called "annuals" because in the colder countries, where their study began, a new crop of these plants is produced annually, during each growing season. In Singapore growth continues all round the year, so the term has little meaning as most of these plants only survive for a few months. "Ephemerals" would be a better name.

Most weeds of cultivated areas are ephemerals, because most herbaceous crops are short lived, and the ground is only left undisturbed for short periods, during which the weed must produce seed if it is to reproduce. Such weeds tend to prosper if they produce copious seeds with adequate means of dispersal and the ability to survive in the dormant condition.

Shrubs and trees may quickly invade such abandoned land if the seeds are wind-borne like the African Tulip Tree (p. 124) or are transported by birds or bats like the Straits Rhododendron (p. 98). One of the commonest treelets which quickly occupies wasteland, especially in the city, is the so-called Cherry Tree (*Muntingia calabura*). Other "pioneer species" of quick-growing and sun-loving trees are *Macaranga* spp. (p. 124), and *Trema* spp., which is particularly important in Peninsular Malaysia.

Fire is an important agent which influences subsequent vegetation, although it is under better control these days when bonfires are illegal. Fire selectively encourages herbs with underground rootstocks like lallang (p. 78). It also encourages shrubs like the Straits Rhododendron and some trees which can sprout from their unburned bases. Such degraded vegetation persists over long periods if fires are sufficiently frequent.

Another kind of scrub and grassland vegetation used to develop under the influence of browsing cattle when these were permitted in Singapore. Lallang cannot withstand repeated cutting or grazing of the young shoots, so was replaced by short swards of more tolerant grasses. Bushes like *Lantana* (p. 98) and Straits Rhododendron, which are avoided by cattle, grew up and formed bushy clumps between the grassy cattle walkways.

BELUKAR OR SECONDARY FOREST

Abandoned land quickly regenerates to form a secondary forest which is usually known by its Malay name *belukar*. Most of the woodland in Singapore is *belukar*, including the Catchment Area, except for small patches of the original forest. A large area of *belukar* can be seen adjoining the Botanic Gardens on the other side of Tyersall Avenue.

Trees which establish themselves in *belukar* are the quick-growing, light-demanding pioneer species. They form a dense thicket in which shade-loving tree species can develop. However, the species which actually do so are those whose seeds reach the place, mainly wind-borne seeds or those whose fruits are eaten by birds.

Belukar contains only a limited number of tree species compared with virgin forest. In Singapore it is likely to be completely devoid of Dipterocarps, whose seeds are produced at intervals of several years, and can only be scattered for short distances by the wind. They also only remain viable for a few days.

Belukar may contain stands of trees which are of similar height, with one or a small number of

species dominant, wherever the whole of an area was left to regenerate simultaneously. In other areas, with a different history, it may have a patchy appearance with stands of trees interspersed with patches of trees, shrubs and giant herbs such as gingers. It is very variable.

There may be a tangled growth of climbers, like Mile a Minute, *Thunbergia grandiflora* (p. 132), members of the Morning Glory family and Rattan Palms. These climbers may be so dense as to interfere greatly with the growth of the trees by shading them. On the other hand, *belukar* is deficient in epiphytes and in plants requiring deep shade.

In secondary forest there is usually sufficient light reaching the ground to allow the growth of dense vegetation which is diffi-cult to walk through, unlike the situation in the darker primary forest, which is easy to penetrate.

Although *Albizia* trees may reach a height of 20 m. in four years and may ultimately reach a height of 45 m., *belukar* is usually not a very tall kind of forest, and the complex stratification typical of primary forest does not develop. The lower levels are warmer and drier and so are poorer in

Left: *A giant rattan palm* (Plectocomia griffithii) *on the edge of the* belukar *beside MacRitchie Reservoir. It climbs by means of nasty, recurved hooks on its switch-like leaf mid-ribs. Around it are* resam *ferns.*

Below: *The* Albizia *often towers above the other trees on roadside verges and in cemetaries. There is a giant West Pacific epiphytic climber — Devil's "Ivy"* (Scindapsus aureus) — *climbing up it.*

shade and moisture-loving herbs than primary forest. It is devoid of palms except the Fishtail Palm (p. 120) and some rattans.

Belukar may burn in dry weather, while primary forest cannot except perhaps after the most severe drought. However, when the adjacent *belukar* is burned, a narrow strip along the edge of the primary forest is also burned.

When *belukar* develops on poor soils, such as those on the shale and sandstone of Kent Ridge, an impoverished scrub develops. It is characterised by trees and shrubs such as *Tiup-tiup* (*Adinandra dumosa*), some species of fig, *Simpoh Air* (p. 98) and the Straits Rhododendron (p. 98), together with the scrambling *Resam* ferns (p. 40) and the Drooping Clubmoss (*Lycopodium cernuum*). It has been perpetuated by repeated fires.

The *Resam* ferns *Dicranopteris linearis* and *Gleichenia truncata* are two similar ferns which grow freely in dense masses up to two metres high on impoverished sites. They produce such dense shade that it is virtually impossible for tree seedlings to establish themselves under them. However there can be no such thing as invulnerability in the plant kingdom — only different survival strategies. *Resam* cannot itself grow in the deeper shade of trees, and in the Catchment Area it can sometimes be seen as a thin growth straggling up the lower branches, just holding its own. The stems creep on the soil and are killed by burning or cutting. *Resam* covers extensive areas in some of the most impoverished parts of the Catchment Area, and its wiry tangle makes such places extremely unpleasant to explore.

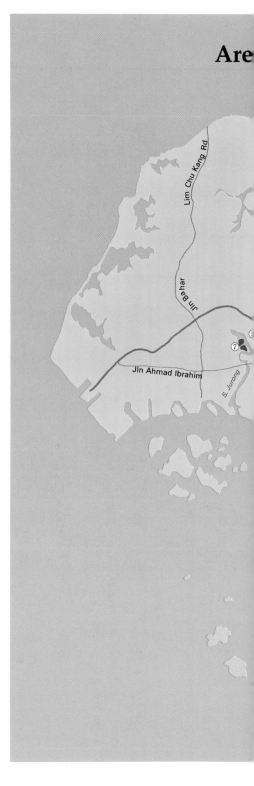

Are

Botanical Interest in Singapore

KEY:

1	Botanic Gardens	10	Labrador Park
2	Bukit Timah Nature Reserve	11	MacRitchie Reservoir
3	Changi Beach	12	Mandai Orchid Garden
4	Chinatown	13	Nee Soon swamp forest
5	Chinese Garden	14	Pasir Ris mangrove
6	Istana	15	Seletar Reservoir
7	Japanese Garden	16	Sister Islands
8	Kent Ridge	17	Thomson Road nurseries
9	Kranji Reservoir	18	Zoological Gardens

URBAN SURVIVORS

The more frequent and severe the interference with vegetation, the more it is degraded and the fewer the species that survive. This is most obvious with trees, where timber that has taken hundreds of years to grow can be felled in a few minutes. However, trees that can regenerate from their cut bases have an advantage over the others, and cutting such trees leaves the soil intact.

Generally speaking, short-lived herbs will regenerate from their lower ends if they are cut early in life, while their survival is not at stake if seed has already set. Furthermore, the seeds may be surviving in the soil and opening up the ground may encourage them to germinate. It is clear that a short life, in which vast numbers of seeds are produced, is one successful strategy for opportunistic plants. Breaking up the soil surface by *changkul* or hoe kills such short-lived herbs, as their roots do not store nutrients. However, plants with underground creeping rootstocks like lallang survive such treatment so are selectively encouraged.

Strangling figs (Ficus microcarpa *on left and a luxuriant* F. benjamina *on right) are among the most common vegetation found on old buildings in Chinatown.*

Resistance to predators and parasites seems to be a factor in survival. Native plants have reached some accommodation with them. When a plant is introduced to a new region it may not be able to survive the local enemies. On the other hand, an introduced species may find itself without enemies in the country to which it has been brought. It may then multiply out of control and become a serious weed. This seems to be the case with several plants introduced from tropical America, such as the Water Hyacinth (p. 68), *Lantana* (p. 98), and Mile a Minute. *Eupatorium odoratum* is spreading down the Malay Peninsula from the north, but it has not become a pest in Singapore because it does not seem to flower here.

GRASSLAND VEGETATION

Plants which are well adapted to frequent breaking of their stems must be capable of branching after cutting. In the past, cropping by grazing animals was the principal means by which this happened, but nowadays, grasslands in Singapore, which are increasing in area, are mainly a response to mowing machines.

Grasses are especially well adapted to cutting and trampling, as cut leaves continue to grow from the base. Only a few species, like lallang and some giant grasses, can be eliminated by repeated cutting.

A thick growth of grasses, with its mass of roots growing in compacted earth, forms a definite "skin" on the soil. It discourages erosion, encourages water runoff and has some effect in discouraging soil creep and earth slides.

The Padang and hundreds of other playing fields, parks, roadsides and road dividers outside the city, and the spaces between blocks of Housing and Development Board apartments, are some of the principal grasslands of Singapore.

Grasses produce side stems in the leaf axils. These are short in some species producing tufted grasses like Lemon Grass or *Serai* (*Cymbopogon nardus*). Others have stems which creep just above the surface of the ground and are anchored by tufts of roots at each node. It is these creeping grasses which can survive repeated cutting, and form a dense mat.

The predominant short grass is Carpet Grass (*Rumput Parit*, *Axonopus compressus*) with broad, wavy-edged leaf blades. It is a native of the Caribbean, but there are many other species. Though creeping grasses dominate, there are many other herbs in the grassland. Some of these, such as a lesser clubmoss *Selaginella*

Evening falls on the reclaimed land beyond Sheares Bridge. Grasses are often the first to colonise such places, but casuarinas (in silhouette near bridge) are planted.

ciliaris, are too low to be mowed, as are some small flowering herbs like the tiny Creeping Pennywort (*Hydrocotyle sibthorpioides*). The Elephant's Foot (*Tutup Bumi, Elephantopus scaber*) has rosettes of leaves pressed against the ground. The upright flowering stems are cut but regenerate freely. The Sensitive Plant (p. 80) and Coat Buttons (*Kancing Baju, Tridax procumbens*) are common in drier grasslands. They survive mowing well as a large part of the spreading branches are too low to be cut.

RECLAIMED LAND AND BUILDING SITES

When travelling around Singapore roads it is possible to see large areas of more or less bare ground where hills are razed or where land has been cleared for building, while much of the coastline is in various stages of reclamation from the sea. These areas start out devoid of vegetation, but if left alone quickly become covered.

Reclaimed land is either produced by moving subsoil from hills, or by pumping in sand in the form of a slurry. The new ground is usually compacted. It is an inhospitable environment at first, and the development of plant cover is further delayed by the scarcity of seeds. The plants which first establish themselves are grasses and some annuals, together with the thorny treelet *Mimosa pigra*, which has pink flowers and slowly responding sensitive leaves.

On coastal reclamations coastal trees are usually planted in due course, such as Casuarinas, Sea Hibiscus (p. 116) and *Acacia au-*

riculaeformis, which has been planted extensively behind the new beach in Changi. It would be worthwhile planting more species of trees and wild herbs which naturally inhabit such shores. However, some of these are already established, probably from seeds which floated in.

Building sites in areas of urban renewal are rather similar to reclamations. The soil there is not so compacted, so it is more favourable to plant growth. Within months of clearance, these sites are often covered with "cherry trees".

THE VEGETATION OF BUILT STRUCTURES

In the city artificial structures predominate: houses, apartments, roads and footpaths, walls and drains. These are not sterile habitats. Even the pristine whiteness of modern concrete buildings may change to reddish-brown or green owing to the growth of single-celled algae. Strangling figs like the Benjamin Fig, the Sacred Bodh Tree (p. 122) and *Ficus microcarpa* (p. 120) can establish themselves even on new buildings, if there are surfaces moist enough to trap humus-forming mosses as on flat roofs or gutters. They illustrate the fact that plants growing as epiphytes may grow equally well on rocks or masonry, unless they are semi-parasites like mistletoes.

The weathering of cement and mortar, and the development of cracks in concrete, provide excellent bases for some plants. Spontaneous plant life on buildings is at its most prolific in old parts of Chinatown. Besides strangling figs several metres high, it is quite common to see large ferns growing luxuriously, especially where a leaky drain provides an adequate water supply. The Pink Periwinkle (p. 66) sometimes takes root in cracks in masonry.

The sides of old roadside drains which are moist are usually cracked. They may be covered in mosses, if sufficiently shaded, and often contain seedlings of strangling figs, and small herbs of which the commonest is the Artillery Plant (*Pilea microphylla*).

Cracks in the pavement or in the roadside kerbs have their own flora, of which a notable component is *Hedyotis corymbosa* and some annual grasses like the fairylike *Eragrostis tenella*.

These wild herbs growing on damp, shady masonry are, from left to right, Artillery Plant from South America; Hedyotis corymbosa, *which also grows in sunny places; and Yellow Woodsorrel (Oxalis corniculata), one of the few plants in the region which also grow wild in Europe.*

THE VEGETATION OF OLD RESIDENTIAL AREAS

There are areas in Singapore, such as those near the Botanic Gardens and Nassim Road, where large detached houses, "colonial bungalows" or "compound houses", are surrounded by spacious gardens and where the roadside verge is allowed to grow wild. The result is often a very harmonious "countryside" in the sense that it is a blending of human influence and natural growth. Although some encroachments have been made in these areas in the past by blocks of luxury apartments, some of them are likely to persist because of restrictions on newer types of building in certain areas set aside for preservation.

The garden of these bungalows may be formal enough, usually with an extensive lawn, but from the edge of the lawn to the road-

side kerb is a strip of vegetation. Starting from the roadside it may be occupied by shade-tolerant grasses and some herbs, such as the Star of Bethlehem (p. 76). Further in there is a sort of hedge, which is really the no-man's land between the roadside verge and the lawn, both of which are regularly cut. Trees and shrubs can establish themselves there and these are likely to be species whose seeds are distributed by birds. Macarthur's Palm (*Ptychospermum macarthurii*, p. 61 right) and some small bushy figs are common, as well as others like Wild Cinnamon (p. 124) and the African Tulip Tree (p. 124). Some of these may grow into quite big trees, and there may be gaps in the vegetation. I would call it a "now-you-see-it, now-you-don't" hedge, as through it, from time to time, you can catch a glimpse of the stately home behind. It has a natural, or, if you prefer it, an untidy look.

The Botanic Gardens used to be surrounded by such vegetation, but this has been replaced by a tidier, patchy and rather characterless hedge of African Camwood (*Baphia nitida*).

EPIPHYTES

Roadside tree plantings have produced a number of sites which are ideal for the growth of epiphytes. Most of these are ferns (p. 138) and a few are orchids. The Rain Tree from Central America provides ideal conditions for epiphytes as do the native *Eugenia grandis* (*jambu laut*) and the durian (p. 142).

It is not clear why some species are so richly covered with epiphytes. Rough or fissured bark is better than smooth bark, and I suspect that bark which weathers more rapidly, absorbs moisture and encourages the growth of mosses to form humus, is more favourable than the drier and harder bark that encourages the growth of lichens. Lichens do not get covered with other forms of vegetation.

Though most of the hundreds of species of local orchids are epiphytes, only a few of them are common on roadside trees. Outstanding for its commonness, interest and occasional beauty is the Pigeon Orchid (p. 140), which flowers every few months on the same day all over the island. It might be worth publicly announcing the days on which the Pigeon Orchid flowers: many times I have been disappointed to see that I was one day late and all that was left was yesterday's blooms, looking like tiny white upside-down pigeons. But I suppose such announcements would need to be accompanied by exhortations to drivers to keep their eyes on the road — not the orchids!

Unfortunately, in the past many trees have been purposely stripped of their epiphytes in the belief that these are dangerous parasites or that, in some way, they render the tree more liable to rotting. It is true that durian trees, when old and declining, are often covered in epiphytes. But the epiphytes are the effect, not the cause, of the decline. I do not know of evidence supporting the belief that epiphytes growing on roadside tree trunks do harm to trees. Even if there were some slight harm done, I think that the epiphytes should be kept because of their beauty, and because they are a part of nature.

ORNAMENTAL PLANTS
AND GARDENING

The old colonial houses had big gardens in the days when land and labour were cheap, and they were largely inspired by the spacious landscaped surroundings of great British country houses, rather than the dense luxuriance of Singapore. Even the early artists pictured Singapore and Penang as rather open places, curiously reminiscent of English parkland!

Old bungalows with big gardens still survive in certain suburbs of Singapore. The front garden, with its curved driveway, reveals the house across the lawn, usually seen through occasional isolated flowering shrubs, and trees if the garden is big enough. Beds of flowers, such as cannas (p. 86) are usually limited in extent — especially in these days when most people offering their services as gardeners know little or nothing of the art.

Nowadays, most gardens are small. There is usually an area of grass, and some flowering shrubs. There may be banana or papaya plants (p. 144) and one of the smaller fruit trees like guava (*Psidium guajava*) or soursop (*Annona muricata*). Mangos (p. 144) are common though they do not fruit well in Singapore. Ornamental annual flowers are little grown as most do not flower well.

One modern tendency is for an unnecessarily large area to be covered with concrete or tiles. There are several possible reasons for this. Chinese temples provide an example to home owners. With great crowds on festival days, the temple courtyard must be paved if it is not to become a quagmire, and most of the shrubs are grown in large jars. For people moving out from the congested city centre, concrete might seem more civilised or more "natural" than bare earth, which has traditionally been regarded as dirty.

Most people in Singapore are limited in what they can grow, as they live in Housing Board flats. There is the very real danger of flower pots falling and harming people below, and there are no provisions for window-boxes. But a wide variety of plants can safely be grown in containers in common corridors, and in the well-lit kitchen area.

A few of the most shade-tolerant plants can survive in

One of the many scenic spots in the Botanic Gardens. This is the best place to visit for an overview of the variety of plants found in the region as well as those from the other tropical lands.

living rooms, such as several species of *Dracaena*, and the Aroids *Schindapsus aureus* and the elegant Heartleaf Philodendron (*P. oxycardium*), which will grow in water without soil. Home gardening in Singapore is becoming more and more a matter of cultivation in pots, window boxes and hanging baskets.

Hybrid orchids are usually grown in pots, and verandahs of flats and suburban gardens sometimes have a fine display, often in a very confined space. The devoted orchid grower can produce fine blooms by watering twice a day, and by an appropriate regime of fertilisation and repotting. But the lazy orchid lover can still have a beautiful show by

buying orchids in pots as they come into flower. These are not expensive because of the export industry in cut blooms.

Ornamental foliage plants should increase in popularity in the future as most of them tolerate considerable shade and can be grown on verandahs and car ports. They have been rather neglected as garden plants in the past, though I believe that the shade garden with large ornamental leaves best expresses the tropical luxuriance of Singapore.

Miniaturised treelets are increasing in popularity. They are a Chinese invention, better known by their Japanese name of *bonsai*. Some are imported from China; most are homegrown. Wild Water Plum and Singapore Holly (pp. 102 & 106) make the most beautiful *bonsai*. They tolerate the re-

This ornamental palm, Pinanga coronata, *deserves to be more commonly grown in Singapore.*

gime well, have small leaves, and flower freely.

Chinatown, with its scanty plant life, is not completely devoid of domestic cultivation. On verandahs and in back lanes many kinds of plants are cultivated for various purposes. Some have beautiful flowers like *Keng Hwa* (p. 104), many such as Moses in a Basket (*Rhoeo discolor*) are grown for medicinal purposes. Others are also grown for ritual and auspicious purposes, like the pomegranate (p. 14), which is one of the most popular pot plants. A few flavourings are grown, such as the scented Pandanus (*P. amaryllifolius*), and chillies (p. 152) and shallots, where a little goes a long way. These plants are now being grown in flats.

The Malay pot-garden is not seen so often nowadays, as there are few traditional Malay houses left, built of wood and raised on stilts. Typically there is a clear space around the house which is swept every day. Usually there are several rows of plants in front of the house growing in pots or cans, mounted in tiers on posts or planks. Besides this, there may be trailing plants hanging from the eaves in containers.

As for the special gardens of Singapore, the Botanic Gardens is obviously the most interesting (see following double page). Most of the cultivated plants are labelled with scientific names, family name and country of origin. There is an outstanding collection of orchid cultivars, and grouped collections of palms, conifers and many other types of plant.

The Istana Negara, official Residence of the President of the Republic, is the old Government House dating from 1869, and has by far the biggest and finest of colonial gardens. It is open on most public holidays.

The Chinese and Japanese Gardens in Jurong have been laid out by experts in two of the greatest gardening traditions in the world, with architecture to match. However, they illustrate the difficulty of producing a garden in one idiom, in a climate where the original species of plants cannot be grown.

The Singapore Zoological Gardens are on a wooded peninsula jutting into Seletar Reservoir, and the standard of gardening justifies its inclusion in the list. Near by are the Mandai Gardens. These are at the same time a pioneering venture in commercial orchid cultivation and a nursery for other ornamental plants, and the most beautiful labour-of-love by John and Amy Ede.

Tristellateia australasiae

A Walk through the Botanic Gardens

*(Numbers in **bold** refer to those shown on the map.)*

We enter the Main Gate and walk along the road. On the left is a group of Sago Palms (**1** *Metroxylon sagu*) and a couple of young *Shoreas* (**2**). Further down is a strangling fig (**3** *F. microcarpa*, p. 120), *Canna* hybrids (**4** p. 86) and a Marsh Garden (**5**). On the right of the road (**6**) are more Dipterocarp trees. We reach the Main Lake (**7**) and its island (**8**) with exuberant swamp vegetation including Nibong Palm (*Oncosperma tigrillarium*), *Simpoh Air* (p. 99) and a *Pandanus*. At the far end is the Lotus Pond (**9** p. 69), and the Miniature Waterfall (**10**) in its own humid, little woodland with shade plants.

Skirting a lawn (**11**) inhabited by topiary animals, we come to a road with Cannonball Trees (**12** *Couroupita guianensis*) flaunting their strange and beautiful flowers. On our right, behind the *Heliconias* (**13**) are forest trees with some Giant Fan Palms (*Johannesteijsmannia altifrons*) from Peninsular Malaysia.

Bearing left of the Sealing-wax Palms (**14** p. 122) we come to the Orchid Enclosure (**15**), which contains about 250 kinds of orchid, mainly colourful hybrids. Unfortunately the wild species are no longer in the public viewing areas.

Taking the path to the Sun Rockery (**16**), we come to the Bromeliad Collection (**17**), the Tropical House (**18**), the new Bonsai House (**19**) and the interesting Temperate House (**20**) cooled by powerful air-conditioners and artificially lit. It contains plants and orchids which thrive in a cooler climate, such as Slipper Orchids (*Paphiopedilum*) and Begonias.

Below is Palm Valley (**21**) and the Second Lake (**22**) with its waterlilies, including the giant *Victoria amazonica*. Skirting the south end we come to a small stand of rubber trees and the Para Rubber Monument (**23**). Behind the monument and the Bamboo Collection (**24**) is the underpass leading to the Botanic Gardens Extension (**25**). At (**26**) we can enter the Jungle (**27**) and admire the tree-ferns.

We finally emerge at the Lower Ring Road (**28**) with its collection of climbers (**29**) and Rose Garden (**30**), which has a good display of blooms in spite of the climate. Near by is a large White Chempaka tree (**31** *Michelia alba*) on which is growing a giant Tiger Orchid (*Grammatophyllum speciosum*). We cross a lawn (**32**) planted with many Frangipani hybrids and reach the small Japanese Garden (**33**). Not far away is the Fernery (**34**) and the Plant House (**35**), where we may be lucky enough to witness the flowering of the New Guinea Creeper (pp. 134–5) and will probably see the blue-green hanging flower heads of the Jade Vine (*Strongylodon macrobotrys*).

Crossing the Office Gate Road lined by majestic Royal Palms (*Roystonea regia*) from Cuba, we pass more palms and Cycads (p. 97). At (**36**) there are small trees: Clove, Cinnamon, Coffee and Nutmeg (p. 153), while just behind the Office block (**37**) is a huge *kapok* tree (p. 154).

We go through the office buildings (which house the Library and the Herbarium with its collection of over 650,00 dried plant specimens, many hundreds of which are irreplaceable type specimens from which the species were first described), and come out on the Office Ring Road. On our left are the large leaves of a Teak tree (**38** *Tectona grandis*) and the spreading branches of an Alexandrine Laurel (**39** p. 116). A little further down (**40**) is an offspring of one of the original rubber trees brought to Singapore in 1877. From here it is a few metres to our starting point.

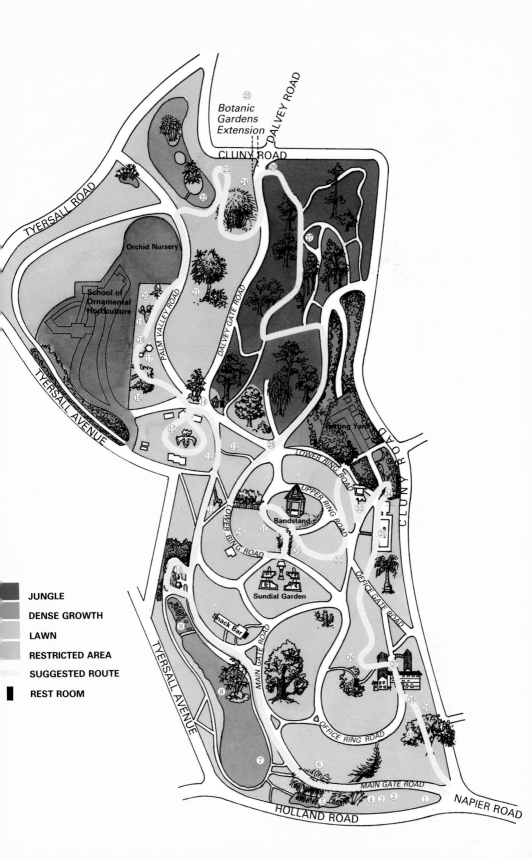

JUNGLE
DENSE GROWTH
LAWN
RESTRICTED AREA
SUGGESTED ROUTE
REST ROOM

THE GREENING OF SINGAPORE

The accelerated development since 1959 has seen great destruction of Singapore's rural vegetation and the disappearance of gardens to make way for offices, factories and flats. However, the government and others have put in an enormous effort to grow trees and shrubs on roadsides, and to develop parks both large and small.

The idea of making Singapore a Garden City started in about 1963. The Prime Minister, Mr. Lee Kuan Yew, inaugurated a tree planting campaign and has nearly always planted a tree himself on Tree Planting Day. The organisational base for the greening of Singapore was the Trees and Parks Section of the PWD and its merger with the Botanic Gardens in 1973, with the Gardens generally providing the research and technical knowledge. This organisation, now the Parks and Recreation Department, has Plant Introduction, Maintenance, Her-

barium, Tissue Culture and other units, and a School of Ornamental Horticulture.

The stated purpose of planting was "... to create and maintain a green and aesthetic environment". It has brought many benefits beyond the beauty of the trees themselves, and the screening and softening effect they have on the appearance of blocks of rectangular high-rise buildings.

The leaves absorb carbon dioxide, and produce oxygen as a by-product of photosynthesis. By their shade and by evaporating water, they provide a cool outdoor environment free from glare. The leaves absorb sound, trap dust and intercept some of the rain, thereby diminishing surface run-off. The timber produced will certainly come to be recognised as a valuable resource in the future, as the over-familiar *Angsana* tree (p. 59) is *Narra*, National Tree of the Philippines, from which the finest furniture is made, and there are Singapore roads lined with broad-leaved mahogany (*Swietenia macrophylla*).

The greening of Singapore has involved innovative approaches. Official encouragement of gardening met with an enthusiastic response from the people. For a

A road-divider along the Expressway to Changi. Early planting and the humid climate ensures that even the newest roads are lined with trees, in this case, the Rain Tree (Samanea saman). For the extensive plantings on roadsides, the funds available (currently about $30 million a year) have to be stretched as far as possible.

period there was even an element of income-tax relief for expenses for gardens facing main thoroughfares, later withdrawn as it was felt to have achieved its aims.

Extensive use is made of "instant trees" such as *Angsana*, which can take root when large branches are planted. Roots and shoots appear in a matter of days and they develop attractive crowns within a year or two.

More recently, vacant plots of idle government land have been planted with trees, producing pleasant woodlands and providing nurseries from which well matured trees can be transplanted to line the roads when they are

A great deal of care is lavished on the plants in the Botanic Gardens, and those in the Bonsai House need to be trimmed regularly to keep their shape.

needed. Besides this many permanent mini-parks have been developed, and green, open and shady places have appeared in parts of Chinatown where there was no green before. In the early days of the campaign such extensive use was made of trees such as *Angsana* and Rain Tree that there was criticism of the resulting monotony, so recently the tendency has been to increase the number of species used for planting. Over a hundred species of trees are now planted, of which only about 15 are indigenous.

Efforts have been made to provide adequate ventilation for tree roots by prohibiting the concreting of the ground surrounding roadside trees. Extensive use is made in footpaths and car parks of perforated concrete slab "ecobricks" which allow roots to

breathe and grass to grow, albeit at some hazard to the wearers of high heels.

At the same time an effort is made to avoid the unnecessary felling of more mature roadside trees. Thus, where a road is being converted to dual carriageway, the trees are left in place, beside the old carriageway, and a new carriageway built to one side, and a third row of trees is planted on its far side.

Pedestrian footbridges over busy roads give us the chance to walk among trees, not merely under them. Where the bridges are not shaded, they are covered in masses of flowering vegetation. On the older wood and iron bridges climbers are often grown. On the more modern concrete footbridges, the usual practice is to grow bougainvilleas (p. 136) in concrete containers on the spans and Dwarf Fig up the pillars.

Lamp-posts in some parts of Singapore are festooned with flowering climbers, which grow up a cylinder of steel mesh. This surrounds the lamp-post but stops short of the top so that branches do not obscure the light.

The greening of flyovers is a problem because of water supply and the deep shade under the bridges. Nevertheless, flyovers are often veritable gardens, with plants like the Dwarf Fig (*Ficus pumila*) climbing up the concrete, with trees and shrubs planted beside the flyover, and shade plants growing in the darker places. At ground level the outline of stark concrete is softened, and the motorist looks out over treetops as he flies over. The most recent research is into methods of growing vegetation in underground stations of the Mass Rapid Transit system.

There is no doubt that the greening of Singapore has been a great success and has done much to improve the environment and hence the quality of life. But it is not surprising that a well-organised, comprehensive programme should impose a degree of uniformity on the landscape. This can be defended on grounds of style, but it does also lead to monotony.

As the main battle has been won, I would hope for new developments in the future, such as a bolder policy of experimental planting of the many exotics which are being introduced — particularly those from neigh-

The beautiful but short-lived flowers of the Angsana (Pterocarpus indicus) are occasionally seen on the older trees after a long dry spell. They fall in a few days.

bouring countries — rather than relying on plants which are proven successes. Secondly, in a situation where natural vegetation is inevitably being destroyed, I would like to see greater effort to preserve what remains and to plant species native to Singapore or at least to the region. We hear much of the conservation of rare and threatened species. Perhaps now is the time to encourage some wild plants by methods of horticulture and silviculture, and by selecting large or free-flowering variants.

I hope one day that many of Singapore's roads will be lined by tall groves of beautiful and valuable Dipterocarp trees. This may seem impossible, but it was successfully undertaken in what is now Ho Chi Minh City, albeit using different species in a different climate.

A tall, straight and uniform avenue of trees is a splendid thing, and it is easy to plan and maintain. But it is monotonous and most unnatural in Singapore, where the original forest was so complex. I hope that species diversity will be maintained and encouraged, at least on most of the roadsides where present tendencies seem to be in the opposite direction.

To summarise, the situation today is that there are only small areas of the original vegetation left, and these are under great pressure. Most of the surviving woodlands are secondary growth following original clearing of the land.

There has been enormous change in the plant life of the rest of Singapore, where the environmental impact of development has been heavy and the humanised landscape of the semi-natural countryside has almost disappeared. Most plant species have diminished in numbers and some have become extinct. However many adaptable species have prospered as weeds, a few to the extent that they can be considered plagues.

On the credit side there has been a successful effort to plant and maintain trees, shrubs and grassland, by the roadsides and in parks and housing estates. Most of the planting has been with plants of foreign origin, and the original green mantle has become multi-coloured, with flowering trees and shrubs and plants with leaves of brilliant hue. The roadsides are more colourful than ever before. But the nature lover, though grateful for all this worthwhile effort, cannot but mourn the passing of natural vegetation, in all its complexity and tangled splendour.

I would like to make a plea for naturalism. I hope that effort will be made to conserve existing vegetation in areas under development, to favour local or regional species and to encourage the sort of plant life which is natural in this balmy climate.

At the edge of busy Orchard Road where once there were old office blocks, a mini-park has been created to provide a peaceful oasis. This roadside park is unusual in that it has a waterlily pond and many species of plant , including Yellow Saraca, Sanchezia, Sui-mei *and Macarthur's Palm.*

Following double page: *The beautiful, bat-pollinated, nocturnal flowers of* Sonneratia caseolaris *may well be a sight of the past as the last few stretches of mangrove where it grows are cleared for development.*

Abbreviations used in the section

FJ	Flora of Java
FM	Flora Malesiana
FT	Flora of Thailand
HT	Hortus Third
RFM	A Revised Flora of Malaya
TCD	Tropical Crops Dicotyledons
TCM	Tropical Crops Monocotyledons
TFM	Tree Flora of Malaya

Species

The enlargement factor for each photograph has been given at the end of the entry — life-size is represented as: x 1.

SUBMARINE AND SEASHORE HERBS

1 **Cryptocoryne ciliata** *(Araceae). The flowe*
ing stem of the **Mangrove Cryptocoryne** *is sho*
and the long tubular spathe has coarse fringi
hairs. The compound fruit is nearly spherical a
splits open to reveal large, green, fleshy, ov
seedlings looking like little artificial Christm
trees wrapped in transparent plastic. When sh
they float, and the outer covering bursts. T
"branches" straighten out and each "Christm
tree" comes to rest on the mud on its flatten
base. Roots grow from the base and leaves devel
from the top. It grows in brackish water betwee
the tidemarks. × ½ (FJ, v.3, 12

2 **Acanthus ilicifolius** *(Acanthaceae).* **Holl**
leaved Acanthus *(Jeruju Putih) is a stiff, sem*
woody plant about 1 m. tall which grows on m
near the high tidemark, sometimes covering lar
areas. The shiny leaves bear spines at their edg
and resemble those of the unrelated Europe
holly and thistle, while other leaves may be alm
spineless. The leaves can excrete salt, which can
seen as white crystals on the upper side of t
leaves after a spell of dry weather. Some botani
have described 3 species; the other two ha
whitish flowers. × ⅖ (FJ, v.2, 25

3 **Caulerpa racemosa** *var.* **clavifera** *(Chlor*
phyta). **Bunch of Grapes Seaweed** *is a creepin*
edible seaweed found growing on the coral reefs
the southern islands. ×

4 **Enhalus acoroides** *(Hydrocharitaceae).* **Gia**
Seagrass *(Setul or Jerangau Laut) is the largest*
all submarine flowering plants. It grows (
protected muddy or coral-sand coasts near the lo
water tidemark. Leaves, about 1 m. long by 2 c
wide, grow from a buried rhizome covered wi
stiff black fibres. Male and female flowers are (
different plants and mature when low water spri
tides occur about 4 p.m. Male plants (as show
here) produce large numbers of small whi
flowers which blow freely over the water wh
their hairlike stems break. Both the male and t
larger, green, 3-petalled female flowers float,
they have water-repellent surfaces. The develo
ing fruit — which is edible and squishy like t
seeds of a cucumber — is brought to the sea bott
by its coiling stem. × 2 (FM, v.5, 4C

1▲ 2▼

▲3 ▼4

65

HERBS OF SANDY SHORES

5 Ipomoea pes-caprae *ssp.* **brasiliensis** *(Con volvulaceae)*. **Sea Morning Glory** *(Tapak Kuda is the most important coloniser of many tropica beaches round the world. Its creeping, rootin, stems often form dense patches which hold dow, the sand and produce humus. The leaves vary i, shape (pes-caprae means "goat's foot"), and th plant is used as a purgative and for other purpose in Malay medicine.* × ¼ (FM, v.4, 475

6 Canavalia maritima *(C. rosea; Papilion aceae)*. **Greater Sea Bean** *(Kacang Laut o Kacang Rang-rang) is a species which trails o the sandy shore, while most of its Pea-flowe relatives are twiners. In this respect, it resemble the Sea Morning Glory. Its flowers and youn, seeds are edible, but care should be taken as th rather similar seaside climber C. microcarpa, wit pointed leaflets and inflated pods, is said to b poisonous.* × ⅖ (FJ, v.1, 633; v.3, 651

7 Wedelia biflora *(Asteraceae)*. **Sea Oxey** *(Pokok Serunai) is a sprawling plant with thick corky, 3-cornered, single-seeded floating fruit, and it can grow on sandy or muddy coasts. Th leaves are quite variable and are semi-succulent i places where they are exposed to salt spray. It ha been used for medicinal purposes.*

A Caribbean relative, W. trilobata, with shin leaves and orange-yellow flower heads, is ofte grown as it is a strong and vigorous climber whic covers ground and can stand both full sun an deep shade. × 4 (FJ, v.2, 404

8 Catharanthus roseus *(Vinca rosea, Lochner rosea; Apocynaceae)*. **Pink Periwinkle** *(Tal Ayam) is a shrubby herb of up to 60 cm. high wit woody stem bases in older plants. Though som times called the Madagascar Periwinkle, it believed by some to be of Caribbean origin. It common on sandy tropical beaches around th world, and is popular in tropical gardens as flowers continuously. A white-flowered variant common. Like most members of the Frangipan family, it is poisonous and because of its bitt taste, the plant is avoided by cattle. It contain many alkaloids. Two of these, vincristine an vinblastine, are valuable drugs used in the trea ment of cancer of the embryonic membranes, an acute leukaemia. They are only present in minut quantities in the plant — about two parts pe million. In Africa and the Caribbean, it is used as folk remedy for diabetes mellitus.* × 1¼ (FJ, v.2, 22

5▲ 6▼

▲7 ▼8

67

9▲

10▲ 11▼

WATER PLANTS

9 Eichhornia crassipes *(Pontederiaceae).* **Wate**
Hyacinth (Keladi Bunting*) was introduced from*
Brazil near the end of the 19th century. It is now a
serious pest in most tropical countries, covering
large areas of quiet fresh waters, interfering with
navigation and shading out other plants. In
Singapore it was cultivated as pig food, but has
been a serious nuisance in Kranji Reservoir. It has
no local enemies except man, and is the only large
herb which floats on the water surface unattached
to the bottom. It is buoyed by its swollen, hollow
leafstalks.   × ⅓ (FM, v.4, 259

10 Limnocharis flava *(Butomaceae).* **Yellow**
Bur-head *is a native of S. America, but it is now*
quite common in marshy places. Like many marsh
plants it has soft, fleshy leaves and air-containing
stems. It is edible.   × ¼ (FJ, v.3, 2

11 Nymphoides indica (Limnanthemum in
dicum; *Gentianaceae). The floating leaf blades of*
the **Water Gentian** *resemble those of a small*
waterlily, but they have short leaf stems and long
stalks anchoring them to the mud. The stems break
easily and plantlets, each with a single leaf and
numerous flowers, can float away. It is common in
the protected parts of MacRitchie Reservoir.
          × ⅗ (FJ, v.2, 441

12 Nelumbo nucifera (Nelumbium nelumbo
Nymphaeaceae). Unlike other waterlilies, the
Sacred Lotus (Teratai or Seroja*) has long, blunt*
spined flower- and leafstalks which are usually
raised above water level, and the leafstalk i
attached near the middle of the leaf blade. It i
especially loved by Buddhists, for whom the flowe
represents the perpetual cycles of reincarnation
Flowers open in the morning and the petals fall in
the afternoon. The seed-like fruits are embedded on
the flat top of the conical receptacle. They are
eaten raw, when unripe, or cooked, when ripe. The
hollow rhizomes are formed like a string o,
sausages, and are boiled or candied and eaten. The
leaves are used to wrap food, and contain a milky
juice. In Singapore the lotus grows throughout the
year, but where there is a distinct cold or dry
season, it may have a period of dormancy.
          × ½ (FJ, v.1, 148

FOREST HERBS

13 **Didymocarpus platypus** *(Gesneriaceae)*
This **Broad-leaved Didymocarpus** *is a rather*
woody-stemmed perennial which grows in the
Bukit Timah Nature Reserve. It has a crown of
hairy leaves and flowers profusely but infrequent-
ly. There are large numbers of species in the region
and the colour patterns of the flowers show
variations from place to place.   × ¼

14 **Tacca integrifolia** *(T. cristata; Taccaceae)*
The flowering stem of the **Black Lily** *(Keladi*
Murai) bears a series of purplish-black flowers
with outwardly-curved petals and sepals. The
flower head is surrounded by 3 sets of bracts. The
outermost two bracts, one above and one below
are broad and purple (not shown in this photo-
graph). Inside this are two tall, narrow, upright
bracts forming a hood over the flowers. The
innermost bracts are the numerous white, hanging
threads.   × ¼
The related T. leontopetaloides is Tahiti
Arrowroot. Its starchy tubers need special treat-
ment before they are safe to eat. It grows wild on
dry coasts in the region.   (FM, v.7, 809–11)

15 **Hornstedtia scyphifera** *(Zingiberaceae)*
Great Spindle Ginger *is a large ginger with*
characteristic ginger-type stems up to 5 m. tall.
The rhizomes typically grow slightly above ground
level, supported by stilt roots. The flower head is
borne on a short stalk and enclosed in a spindle-
shaped series of overlapping mottled bracts with
tubular flowers issuing from the top of the spindle.
It can always be found flowering somewhere in the
Bukit Timah Nature Reserve.   × ⅔

16 (following pages) **Selaginella willdenowii**
(Selaginellaceae). A straggling relative of the
ferns, the **Peacock Fern** *(Paku Merak) has a row*
of larger leaves and a row of small leaves on each
side of its stems. This arrangement allows a very
efficient interception of light. The leaves appear
blue when frontally lit, but the blue colour
disappears under water, so is not due to pigment,
but rather to the structure of the cell surface which
selectively absorbs the red light rays needed for
photosynthesis. The convex cell surface also acts
as a lens to concentrate light on the chlorophyll.
This plant therefore seems to be well adapted to
life on the poorly-lit forest floor, although it does
not need deeper shade than other plants.
In the bottom right-hand corner of the picture
are the cone-like strobili, with a spore-forming
organ under each small leaf.   × 1½ (FT, v.3, 19)

13▲ 14▼

SHADE HERBS

17 **Costus speciosus** (*Zingiberaceae*). The stems of the **White Costus** (Setawar) *may be 2-3 m. tall, with spirally arranged leaves, topped by a flower head. The mass of calyxes and associated bracts looks like a little spiky red pineapple measuring about 10 x 5 cm. One corolla lobe, the pearly-white lip, is greatly enlarged and has a yellow base; it forms a platform for the large female Carpenter Bees which visit it. It is both wild and cultivated in Singapore and flowers freely all the year round. Unlike most members of the Ginger family, the plant has no aromatic smell, but contains the steroid diosgenin, which can be used as a raw material in the production of synthetic sex hormones.* × ⅓ (FJ, v.3, 76)

18 **Alpinia javanica** (*Zingiberaceae*). **Great Javanese Alpinia** (Lengkuang or Tepus Putih) *is a moderate-sized (3 m. tall) ginger which grows in clumps. Its has the typical ginger growth form with slender, curving stem and large elongated leaves arranged alternately on each side. Its leaves are up to 90 cm. long with fine hairs on the underside. The flower heads at the top of the stems are typically drooping. It often grows in rather disturbed places. Its spherical green fruit is 2.5 cm. in diameter.* × ⅓ (FJ, v.3, 48)

19 **Asystasia gangetica** (A. coromandeliana; *Acanthaceae*). **Asystasia** (Akar Ruas-ruas) *is a slender-stemmed herb which scrambles upwards when supported by vegetation. It was introduced from India because of its showy flowers but has run wild. There are several genetic variants with pale yellow, white, pink, mauve or violet corollas, and the pale yellow is the common "wild" type.*

The native A. intrusa, with a smaller white corolla bearing a blue patch, is a very common plant in shady disturbed ground in Singapore. × 2

17▲ 18▼

20 **Amorphophallus campanulatus** (*Araceae*). **Elephant-foot "Yam"** (Loki) *is a giant herb with 2-m.-high purple-mottled leafstalks and much-divided leaf blades. After the leaves have died down, the multi-coloured flower head emerges, with thick bell-shaped spathe and short wrinkled spadix bearing minute flowers. It smells of rotting flesh. The stalk lengthens after flowering and bears numerous small fruit. The young leaves can be eaten after thorough boiling. It is not very common in Singapore, but grows in several places north of Mandai Road. Edible varieties are cultivated in Java. Within a year they can produce a tuber weighing 25 kg. — enough to feed a family for over a week!* × ¼ (FJ, v.3, 111)

21 **Laurentia longiflora** (Isotoma longiflora; *Campanulaceae*). **Star of Bethlehem** *is a native of tropical America from Florida to Peru, and it was introduced as an ornamental, but is now most commonly found growing wild in moist, shady places near human settlements. It has a poisonous, acrid, milky juice and a drop of this is said to be able to produce blindness. Even the copious nectar at the base of the long corolla tube has an unpleasant peppery taste. The plant is said to contain alkaloids which can cause paralysis.* × 1 (FM, v.6, 140)

20▲ 21▼

22 Turnera ulmifolia (*Turneraceae*). **Yellow Turnera** (Holy Rose or Lidah Kucing) *is a herb with a woody stem base and reaching a height of nearly 1 m. It grows wild in dry places, often under shade, and is common at the east end of the island. It was introduced from tropical America, probably because of its showy flowers, which close in the afternoon.*

Another relative, T. subulata, *grows in sunny places. It has cream-coloured flowers with almost-black centres.* × ⅖ (FJ, v.1, 180)

23 Blechnum orientale (*Dennstaedtiaceae*). *Known variously as Paku Ikan, Paku Ular and Paku Lipan, this common fern of sunny and slightly shady places will not grow in deep forest shade, unlike most of the ground-fern species in Singapore, which live in shady wooded areas. The fronds can be up to 1.8 m. long, and are only subdivided once into pinnae. The young shoots can be eaten. In the photograph part of a tree fern,* Cyathea sp., *can be seen on the left, while the large, arrow-shaped leaves of an* Alocasia sp. *and the small heart-shaped leaves of a pepper species are shown on the right.* × ¹⁄₁₀ (RFM, v.2, 446)

▲22 ▼23

SUN-LOVING HERBS

24 Kalanchoe pinnata (Bryophyllum calycinum; *Crassulaceae*). The **Air Plant** is often called Life Plant by schoolchildren (Sedingin is the Malay name). This upright, slightly branched plant has simple or pinnate fleshy leaves with indentations from which plantlets can develop. Probably of African origin, it grows both wild and cultivated. Traditionally-minded Malays believe it has magical and medicinal value. × ½ (FJ, v.1, 202)

25 Imperata cylindrica (*Poaceae*). **Lallang** (Lalang) is a common plant of well-drained open spaces, and is encouraged by burning, which does little damage to its underground creeping stems while provoking flowering. Since burning destroys the other plants around while leaving the lallang unharmed, it leads to the permanent establishment of this grass. Lallang cannot, however, tolerate frequent cutting or grazing of the tender young shoots. Vast areas of SE Asia, especially those places having a dry season, are now covered with lallang. In S. Bali, where land is scarce, lallang is a valuable resource as it is used for thatch and can be grown in the ravines. The rhizome has been used by Chinese as a diuretic. The illustration shows the wind-borne seeds in the foreground with the mauvish flowers above.   (FJ, v.3, 583)

26 Asclepias curassavica (*Asclepiadaceae*). The upright, slightly branched **Orange Milkweed** (Bunga Mas) originally came from tropical America, but is now naturalised all over the region in sandy places. The name "milkweed" comes from the milky latex produced by members of this family. Milkweeds are poisonous because they contain cardiac glycosides, but they are not a danger to cattle, which avoid them. The Orange Milkweed and the Giant Milkweed are the host plants of the Tiger Butterfly, Danaus chrysippus. Birds do not eat the butterflies because they have absorbed the poisons from the milkweed. The potential of the milkweed as a drug plant is being investigated.   × 2 (FJ, v.2, 251)

24▲ 25▼

27 Ageratum conyzoides (*Asteraceae*). *White Weed* (Rumput Tahi Ayam), *a native of tropical America, is a common short-lived weed in open, disturbed ground in the tropics. The flower heads may be whitish or mauve and vary greatly in showiness. The leaves are often attacked by a disease which causes them to crinkle and turn yellow.* × ⅔ (FJ, v.2, 377)

28 Mimosa pudica (*Mimosaceae*). **Sensitive Plant** (Touch-me-not or Rumput Malu) *is a low, spreading, rather wiry plant with hairy stems bearing sharp thorns, as barefoot walkers soon discover. This native of tropical America is now a common pan-tropical weed. When shaken, the leaflets and leaves droop in a second; recovery takes a few minutes. This is due to specialised swellings at the base of the moving parts containing cells which leak when physically shocked. Mimosa has been used for treating asthma in the Philippines. The root is rich in tannins and is used for diarrhoea and as a diuretic.* × ³/₅ (FJ, v.1, 561)

29 Cassia mimosoides (*Caesalpiniaceae*). *The* **Mimosa-leaved Cassia** *has tough, upright stems and tiny leaflets that close at night. It is quite common in undisturbed open places. Another form, possibly of the same species, with fewer, larger leaflets is sometimes named C. lechenaultiana.* × ½ (FJ, v.1, 536)

30 Celosia argentea (*Amaranthaceae*). **Fireweed** (or Quailgrass) *is an upright, short-lived plant with green or red stems and leafstalks, and red or white flowers. It often grows on the sites of previous fires. This is the wild type from which the gaudy plumed and cockscomb forms are derived. Cultivated for centuries in China, they are in great demand as pot plants for the Chinese New Year. The young shoots can be eaten.* × ⅓ (FJ, v.1, 234)

31 Physalis minima (*Solanaceae*). **Lesser Bladder Cherry** (Letup-letup) *is a soft-stemmed, short-lived herb up to about 50 cm. tall with small, bell-shaped flowers having pale yellowish corollas and brown-spotted yellow centres. The fruit is a yellow berry completely hidden inside the greatly inflated calyx, which is like a delicate Chinese lantern. Unlike most pan-tropical weeds, it appears to be a native of the region.* × ⅓ (FJ, v.2, 468)

32 Peperomia pellucida (*Piperaceae*). **Common Peperomia** *is a soft, fleshy-leaved, short-lived plant of S. American origin. The frosted appearance of the leaves is due to light reflected from each convex cell wall. It often grows as a weed in flower pots, and in cracks in masonry. It can be eaten raw or cooked, and has a peppery flavour.* × ⅔ (FJ, v.1, 174)

27▲ 28▼

33▲ 34▼

ORNAMENTAL HERBACEOUS ANNUALS

33 Impatiens balsamina *(Balsaminaceae)*. The *Annual Balsam* is a fleshy-stemmed native of Indonesia which grows up to 70 cm. high and wilts quickly when uprooted. The petals may be single or double, and there is a wide range of flower colours: white, pink, violet or purple.

Other Impatiens are the "Busy Lizzies", probably hybrids between species from SE Asia, which make beautiful, free-flowering pot plants. Several species are also found in the spray-moistened places beside waterfalls in SE Asia. × ¾ (FJ, v.1, 249)

34 Tithonia rotundifolia (T. speciosa; *Asteraceae)*. Tithonia, which can grow up to 1.2 m high, is of Mexican origin. The plant is covered in rather short stiff hairs and is very easy to cultivate in sunny places. × ¼ (HT, 1116)

35 Torenia fournieri *(Scrophulariaceae)*. This Torenia *(Blue Wings or Wishbone Flower)* is native to Thailand and Indo-China. It is an upright plant with square, juicy stems and may grow up to 40 cm. high. The flowers have a colour combination probably unique in the plant kingdom. (Other colour variants have predominantly dark pink or white flowers.) The two stamens arch up inside the upper part of the corolla tube and are attached together at the tips. It produces many tiny seeds and they sprout quickly, but the plant can be grown from cuttings too as the stems root freely. It grows best in moist, shady places.

A close relative T. polygonoides *(Malayan Eyebright*, Kerak Nasi) is a small creeping herb growing on lawns. The tubular flower is small 8 mm. in length, with 3 white corolla lobes, a red upper lobe and a yellow centre. (FJ, v.2, 509)

36 Cosmos bipinnatus *(Asteraceae)*. Cosmos is from Mexico. It is a slender, much-branched plant and grows to a height of 1.5 m. This species has thread-like leaflets and pink or purple ray flowers with yellow disc flowers. The young shoots are edible.

Its relative C. sulphureus, *the Orange Cosmos* is different in having broader, more feather-like leaflets and orange flowers. × ¾ (HT, 321)

ORNAMENTAL HERBACEOUS PERENNIALS

37 **Sanchezia nobilis** *(Acanthaceae). This large, bushy plant from S. America has square, jointed, stiff yellowish stems which turn red in the sunlight, and dark green leaves with pale yellow veins. All flowers on one spike face the same way. The corolla is tubular, and flowers are protected by reddish-brown bracts. It can be grown from cuttings* × ⅓ (FJ, v.2, 556)

38 **Crinum asiaticum** *(Amaryllidaceae). The huge, handsome* **Crinum "Lily"** *(Poison Lily or Bakong) may grow up to 1.5 m., and is native to SE Asia. It has an underground bulb and the lower parts of the leaves form stout pseudo-stems. The flowers are delightfully scented. It is commonly grown in gardens and can take a lot of maltreatment. Large types, as pictured here, grow wild in freshwater or brackish swamps, while smaller types grow on dry, sandy seashores. They are poisonous, and are used in traditional medicine.* × ⅓ (FJ, v.3, 136)

39 **Hymenocallis littoralis** *(Amaryllidaceae). Spider "Lilies" are poisonous natives of tropical America. The flowers have filmy and frilly funnel-shaped centres borne on tall, flattened, solid stems. Some species smell delightful in the evening.* × ½

37▲ 38▼

40 Anthurium ferrierense *(Araceae).* Th ancestors of this hybrid, known variously a *Oil-cloth Plant, Painter's Palette,* or simply a *Anthurium,* are tropical S. American epiphyte: A. ornatum *and* A. andreanum, *with rathe short stems anchored by stout aerial roots. It i grown for its brilliant, glistening spathes, whil the male and female flowers borne on the yellov cylindrical stalk, or spadix, are minute. They ar popular as cut flowers as they can last for severa weeks. Like other aroids they are propagated b division, and are best grown in pots with well drained, peaty soil.* × ¾ (FJ, v.3, 10ξ

41 Canna *hybrid* *(Cannaceae). These plants ar probably hybrids of several species which ar natives of S. America. What look like petals ar really staminodes, modified stamens. Only one o its stamens produces pollen.*

The wild form, C. coccinea (C. indica FJ, v.3, 76), *has smaller, scarlet flowers with nar row, upright petals. It is common in old-fashione gardens, and often persists after the house ha been abandoned. Another species,* C. edulis, *ha rhizomes which are eaten in Java, or used t produce an arrowroot starch. Cannas are propa gated from rhizomes.* × ¹

42 Jatropha podagrica *(Euphorbiaceae, **Guatemala Rhubarb** (or Gout Stick) is a slow growing plant up to 1.5 m. high, with one or a fev thick grey stems and spindle-shaped swollen bases The undersides of the leaves are bluish-white. Th male and female flowers are separate, and th plant is usually grown from seed. It is able t withstand rather dry conditions. It and severa shrubby species from Central America are grow in Singapore gardens. They all contain a poisonou protein.*

The Physic Nut, J. curcas, *is a low shrub whic contains a violent purgative. It is similar to J podagrica, but has brownish flowers. It is some times planted as a living fence.* × ²/₅ (FJ, v.1, 494

43 Zephyranthes rosea *(Amaryllidaceae)* Zephyranthes *are of American origin, Z. rose, coming from Cuba. They are often called rain lilie because rain, after a long dry period, brings then into flower. They flower very freely and are ofter used as border plants for flower beds. Species wit white (Z. candida) and yellow (Z. citrina) flower are also cultivated.* × ¾ (FJ, v.3, 134

40▲ 41▼

▲42 ▼43

87

44 **Orthosiphon aristatus** *(O. stamineus; Lamiaceae).* **Cat's Whiskers** *(Kumis Kucing) is a native of SE Asia. This herb grows about 75 cm high. It has a long corolla tube from which projects the 5-cm.-long style and the slightly shorter stamens. The stem and sometimes the leaves may be purplish. It can be confused only with other plants, also called Cat's Whiskers, which have similar long projecting stamens and belong to the Caper family (Capparidaceae). Orthosiphon is used in Chinese medicine for the treatment of diabetes.* × ⅔ (FM, v.8, 380)

45 **Heliconia rostrata** *(Musaceae).* **Hanging Heliconia** *(or Crab's Claws) is a striking-looking plant with its hanging flower heads and brilliantly-coloured bracts. The small, two-lipped greenish-yellow flowers can be seen projecting beyond some of the bracts. The flower heads hang down from the tops of stems about 2 m. high, but the whole plant grows up to 4 m. high.*

All Heliconias are natives of tropical America, where they are pollinated by hummingbirds. In the wild they are important pioneers of forest clearings, like their relatives the bananas in SE Asia.
× ½ (HT, 551)

46 **Heliconia *hybrid*** *(Musaceae). This hybrid of* H. psittacorum *and* H. lathispatha *grows up to 2 m. tall. It resembles its parent, the smaller and more elegant (though less shapely)* H. psittacorum — *commonly misnamed the Japanese Canna. It is propagated by pieces of rhizome.* × 1 (HT, 551)

47 *(following pages)* **Episcia cupreata** *(Gesneriaceae). A native of Columbia, this* Episcia *is a trailing creeper which grows in shady places. It puts out long flexible stalks or runners, at the end of which a plantlet develops. It is free-flowering, easily propagated from plantlets, and looks attractive hanging down from pots or baskets. Several cultivars exist with differently coloured and sometimes patterned leaves.* × 1¼ (FJ, v.2, 532)

44▲ 45▼

CULTIVATED ORCHIDS (ORCHIDACEAE)

48 Dendrobium *Bangsaen Beauty*. This is the progeny of orchid hybrids produced in other countries. It was developed by Prasan Paripoonanonda in Bangkok in 1968 from the hybrids D. Hawaiian Beauty and D. Sunny Red. Its wild ancestors were 3 species of Dendrobium, principally D. phalaenopsis *from Indonesia.* × ½

49 Vanda *Tan Chay Yan*. This hybrid between the hybrid Vanda Josephine van Brero and the wild species Vanda dearii was produced by Mr. Tan Hoon Siang in Singapore in 1949. It was the first local hybrid to achieve major success, and is named after the hybridiser's father, the first man to plant Para Rubber trees on a commercial scale in Malacca in 1896. × ⅓

50 Vanda *Miss Joaquim*. This free-flowering natural hybrid between two species, V. teres *from Burma and* V. hookeriana *from Malaysia, appeared in the garden of Miss Agnes Joaquim in Singapore in 1893. It has been grown extensively for cut flowers, especially in Hawaii. However, as the cut flowers are unusually short-lasting, it has been largely supplanted by other free-flowering hybrids; so in 1981, when it was officially declared the National Flower of Singapore, it was quite difficult to find enough plants to re-introduce it to the people.* × ⅖

51 Phalaenopsis amabilis. *The **Butterfly Orchid** (Anggerek Bulan) is an epiphyte native to the forests of Indonesia, E. Malaysia and the Philippines. The flowers vary in size and in the details of the coloured parts, but the wild type is mainly pure white. It is a parent of many hybrids, mostly with blooms of predominantly pastel colours. It is not easy to grow in Singapore as it needs very free air circulation, and not too much or too little watering.* × ¼ (FJ, v.3, 419)

52 Spathoglottis plicata. *This large and handsome orchid (Lumbah) was a common wild roadside plant with flowers which vary considerably in size. The large-flowered cultivars, like the one in the photograph, are popular garden plants. The leaves are long, slender and pleated, with tips hanging over. The flower heads have purple bracts which turn black when they die.* (FJ, v.3, 332)

48▲ 49▼

▲51 ▼52

53▲

54▲ 55▼

ORNAMENTAL FOLIAGE HERBS

53 Sansevieria trifasciata *var.* **laurentii** *(Agavaceae)*. *The stiff leaves of this native of S. Africa come from the thick rhizome.* **Mother-in-law's Tongue** *can survive severe maltreatment and a new plant can arise from either end of a cut section of a leaf. It contains a sapogenin which ruptures red blood corpuscles.*

There are many varieties and var. laurentii *is distinguished by the yellow borders on its leaves. The flowers are fragrant.* × ⅓ (FJ, v.3, 162)

54 Pseuderanthemum reticulatum *(Acanthaceae)*. **Golden Pseuderanthemum,** *whose leaves have a network of golden veins, is a cultivar derived from the original green-leaved wild form which is a native of the Pacific islands. It is a small shrubby plant which can be grown from cuttings.*
× ⅓ (FJ, v.2, 577)

55 Coleus cultivar *(Lamiaceae)*. Ati-ati *in Malay, many kinds have been developed by hybridisation, using several species of* Coleus *from Indonesia as parents, and they are grown for their brilliantly-coloured leaves. These may have one, two or three colours. The purplish flowers are small and borne on spikes. Unlike most members of this family, the lower lip of the corolla is the longer one, and is boat-shaped.*

Other Coleus *spp. from the region include C. amboinicus (C. aromaticus), whose fleshy, aromatic leaves are used to flavour food, and C. parviflorus (C. tuberosus) from India, which produces aromatic, edible tubers. Both these species have plain green leaves.*

The correct, modern botanical name for Coleus *Plectranthus.* × ½ (FJ, v.2, 63(

56 Caladium bicolor *(Araceae)*. *Originally introduced from S. America because of their beautiful coloured leaves,* Caladiums *have escaped and are now wild in rubber estates. Many cultivars with brightly-coloured and strikingly-patterned leaves have been developed by nurserymen from the original wild type, which has small red and white blotches on the leaves. The flower head with its cream-coloured spathe is not very commonly seen. The plant is propagated by tubers and sometimes the leaves die down for several months, especially during dry periods.* × ³/₅ (FJ, v.3, 122)

SEASHORE SHRUBS AND TREELETS

57 Scaevola taccada (S. sericea; *Goodeniaceae*) *Sea Lettuce* (Ambong-ambong or Buas-bua Laut) *is a common, rather soft-stemmed shrub o very distinctive appearance which grows at the high tidemark of sandy beaches all round the equator. I is the only member of the family native to SE Asia though there are many species in Australia. It fleshy leaves are pale coloured. The corolla tube splits along its upper side when the flower opens and the 5 corolla-lobes are arranged on the lowe. side. The pithy oval berries are about 12 mm. long and they float. A decoction is produced from the roots in the Philippines and used as medicine. The leaves can be smoked as tobacco.* (FT ,v.2, 279.

The threadlike stems of Dodder-laurel (Cas-sytha filiformis *(Lauraceae)* Chemar), *a common seaside semi-parasite, can be seen climbing the plant.* × ⅓ (FJ, v.1, 135.

58 Glochidion littorale (*Euphorbiaceae*). **Jam-bu Kera** *(or Selunsor) is a bushy shrub of sandy shores and, occasionally, mangroves. It grows up to 3 m. in height, and has leathery leaves which turn orange when old. The flowers are small and green. The fruit has a marked dimple at the apex and longitudinal grooves. It splits from apex to base into 10–15 parts, liberating the orange seeds The young red leaves are edible.* × ⅓ (FJ, v.1, 461.

59 Cycas rumphii (*Cycadaceae*). *The primitive Seashore Cycad* (Paku Laut) *has seeds but no flowers. It is a palm-like shrub with beautiful dark, shiny fern-like leaves and a stout, occa-sionally branched trunk. It grows wild on dry exposed coasts, but only planted specimens sur-vive in Singapore. The ovules of the female trees are borne on modified leaves and the ripe ova seeds, about 6 cm. long, hang down. The stamens are borne on spiny scales tightly bunched togethe. to form a cone, like a golden pineapple about 3(cm. high. The seed is rich in starch, but poisonous and contains a carcinogen. It was used as famine food, after repeatedly washing the crushed seeds The soft young leaves can be eaten cooked.*
× ¹⁄₁₀ (FT, v.2, 186.

60 Pandanus odoratissimus (*Pandanaceae*). *The **Common Seashore Screwpine** (Pandanus or Pandan) is a thick-stemmed treelet of rocky or sandy shores. It has a more branched habit than most screwpines and rather greyish-blue spine-edged leaves. The fruit is edible. On Pacific atolls, where there are many variants, it is one of the most important and useful plants in supporting human life.* × ⅛ (FJ, v.3, 202)

57▲ 58▼

97

WILD SHRUBS AND TREELETS

61 Melastoma malabathricum (*Melastoma taceae*). **Straits Rhododendron** (Sendudok) is *a* very variable, free-flowering shrub up to 3 m. tall and covered with small, bristly scales. The ova*l* pulpy fruit, containing many small seeds, i*s* purplish-black and rather tasteless, but childre*n* eat it and it stains their tongues black, hence th*e* name melastoma, Greek for "black mouth". Th*e* sour young leaves can be eaten raw or cooked*.* This shrub is a favourite food of Flowerpecker*s* (Dicaeum *spp.*) and is the host plant for th*e* caterpillars of the Common Sailor, Nepthylas, *a* black-and-white butterfly, and the Grey Coun*t* Butterfly, Tanaecia lepidea. The Straits Rho*-* dodendron tends to be taken for granted, but *it* should be a top priority to select forms with larg*e* flowers and free-flowering habit, now that there i*s* so little of it left by the highways.   × ½ (FJ, v.1, 358*)

62 Lantana camara (*L. aculeata*; *Verbenaceae*)*.* Lantana (Tahi Ayam) is a low, scrambling shru*b* with small blunt spines and a pungent smell rathe*r* like blackcurrants. Introduced as an ornamenta*l* from tropical America, it has since become *a* serious weed as it is shunned by cattle (buffaloe*s* can eat it) and has few insect enemies. Severa*l* colour varieties occur in Singapore, and flower*s* darken as they age. It is sometimes cultivated an*d*

61▲ 62▼

he fruits are edible. The pounded leaves have been used to treat wounds and ulcers and are said to be emetic. × 2 (FJ, v.2, 597)

63 Cassia alata (Caesalpiniaceae). A native of tropical America, **Seven Golden Candlesticks** (Gelenggang) commonly grows wild in disturbed damp places, such as flood plains. It is a short-lived shrub with few, rather coarse branches and grows to a height of 3 m. The flower buds are covered with orange bracts which fall when the flower opens. The leaves are used to treat fungal skin infections. They contain chrysophanic acid, a fungicide. The seeds are small and square, and rattle softly when the winged pod is shaken. They are purgative and vermifuge. × $\frac{1}{12}$ (FJ, v.1, 540)

64 Dillenia suffruticosa (Wormia suffruti-cosa; Dilleniaceae). The **Shrubby Dillenia** (Sim-poh Air) grows up to 5 m. in height and has very characteristic cabbage-like, oval leaves which are slightly toothed and up to 35 cm. long. These are often used to wrap food. The red fruits open before dawn into several segments, exposing the red-fleshed seeds which are so appetising to birds that they are rarely seen. In Singapore it is commonest on eroded hills on Kent Ridge and Pasir Panjang, but it can also grow in swamp forest.
× $\frac{2}{5}$ (TFM, v.1, 192)

▲63 ▼64

FLOWERING SHRUBS AND TREELETS

65 Nerium indicum (N. odorum; *Apocy-naceae*). *This species of* **Oleander** *(Anis) is a native of Asia and is scented, unlike the better known European species* N. oleander. *It is a small shrub, about 4 m. tall, with an upright growth habit and little branching. Besides the wild pink form, there are red and white varieties and some have double flowers. The whole plant is extremely poisonous, and it is said that 3 of the rather small leaves may prove fatal if eaten and that people have died from eating meat cooked on oleander skewers, including some of Alexander the Great's soldiers.* x ³/₅ (FJ, v.2, 240)

66 Ervatamia divaricata (Tabernaemontana coronaria; *Apocynaceae*). **Pinwheel Flower** *(Je-lutong Badak) is probably a native of India. It is common as a small shrub with a rather spreading flat top. The leaves are dark and shiny and contain a poisonous latex. The fragrant flowers are pinwheel-shaped — that is, the corolla-lobes do not radiate straight from the centre, but have a counter-clockwise twist when seen from above. This is due to the way the buds unfold. A double-flowered form is commonly grown.* × ³/₅ (FJ, v.2, 228)

65▲ 66▼

67 Adenium obesum (A. coetaneum; *Apocy-naceae*). *Adenium (sometimes called Japanese Frangipani) is a small, succulent-stemmed treelet with white latex, native to E. Africa and Arabia. It can grow up to 1 m. tall. It has smooth, fleshy stems and can easily be propagated from cuttings. It readily drops its shiny leaves, especially during the flowering season, and even when the weather is not dry. Unlike many succulents, it flowers freely. It needs warmth and drought and is usually grown in pots with well-drained soil. The plant contains the cardiac glycoside echugin, and is used as a fish poison in Africa.* × ³/₅ (HT, 25)

68 Barleria cristata (*Acanthaceae*). *A native of India, the small, leafy* **"Philippines Violet"** *is especially popular in the Philippines. It is often grown as a hedge, though it does not flower well when trimmed frequently. Several flowers grow from the axil of each leaf, but only one opens at a time, and the corolla falls off in the afternoon. The popular name comes from the usual colour of the corolla, though white and two-coloured forms are grown. The funnel-shaped corolla contains co-pious nectar. It is easy to propagate by cuttings.* × 1½ (FJ, v.2, 572)

69 **Bixa orellana** (*Bixaceae*). **Lipstick Tree** (Kesumba) is a native of tropical S. America which grows to a height of about 4 m. The young shoots are covered in dull, dark red scales. It is grown in Singapore for its ornamental fruits which look rather like rambutans (p. 142). The fruit splits into two to reveal the seeds surrounded by the orange-red, creamy-textured aril. This is used as face paint by tribal people and the dye, which is fat-soluble, is nowadays used to colour lipstick and — in minute quantities of course — margarine. It contains bixin, used in Africa as a purgative.

× ½ (FJ, v.1, 281)

70 **Thevetia peruviana** (*Apocynaceae*). **Yellow "Oleander"** (Zetun or Jitong) is a treelet with leaves and a growth habit similar to that of the oleander, though more spreading. It may reach m. in height. The light, 3-cm.-long, green fruit is transversely oval, with a ridge around the middle. The plant exudes a white latex and is so poisonous that a single fruit may prove fatal. It contains the cardiac glucoside thevetin causing vomiting, weakness of the pulse and convulsions.

× ⅗ (FJ, v.2, 233)

71 **Wrightia religiosa** (*Apocynaceae*). **Wild Water Plum** (Sui-mei) is a native of Thailand and W. Malaysia. It is often grown in Thai Buddhist temples. An elegant shrub, up to 2 m. tall, with flat top and rather horizontal or slightly drooping branches, it is easily propagated from cuttings. It seems an "old-fashioned" plant, but has recently come back into popularity. It makes an ideal bonsai with its fragrant and frequent flowers, and should be grown on the balcony of every flat dweller. × 1 (FJ, v.2, 241)

72 **Tecoma stans** (Stenolobium stans; *Bigno-niaceae*). This treelet from tropical America, known as **Yellow Bells**, grows up to 4 m. high. It has rather drooping, pale, pinnate leaves and bears copious branches of hanging bell-shaped flowers several times a year. The fruits contain small winged seeds. × ½ (FM, v.8, 186)

69▲ 70▼

103

73 Calliandra emarginata *(Mimosaceae)*
Several species of these free-flowering tropical American shrubs are grown in the region. The flowers are in dense, spherical heads and have long silky stamens — whence comes the name calliandra, *meaning "beautiful stamens". The* **Red Powder-Puff Plant** *has frequent "flushes" of flowers. The leaves are divided into two parts, each with 3 leaflets.*

Another commonly-grown species is C. surinamensis, which has long white stamens tipped with mauvish-pink, and many small leaflets.

× ⅕ (HT, 200–1)

74 Caesalpinia pulcherrima *(Caesalpiniaceae).*
Peacock Flower *(Jambul Merak or Cana) is a very beautiful and common free-flowering treelet with slightly thorny stems, growing to a height of about 3 m. It is believed to have come from the S. American tropics, but is unknown in the wild state. Besides the usual colour form, which is illustrated, there are yellow- and red-flowered varieties. The young seeds can be eaten raw. It is a host plant of the common Grass Yellow Butterfly,* Eurema hecabe. × ½ (FJ, v.1, 544)

75 Euphorbia pulcherrima (Poinsettia pulcherrima; *Euphorbiaceae*). **Poinsettia** *is a native of Mexico and it grows up to 3 m. tall with rather few upright branches. Like others of the genus, it exudes a milky latex. The insignificant, yellowish flowers grow in clusters at the ends of the branches, surrounded by spectacular, red, leaf-like bracts. It must be grown from cuttings, and there are cultivars with white and pink bracts. In Java the shoots and young inflorescences are eaten, but only after cooking.* × ½ (FJ, v.1, 501)

76 Epiphyllum oxypetalum *(Cactaceae). Singaporeans think of the* **Keng Hwa** *as an essentially Chinese plant, but it, like all other cacti, originated in the Americas, and only reached Singapore via Amoy in 1920. A rather straggling, spineless cactus with flat stems, each having a thickened central rib and two flat fleshy blades, it flowers infrequently. Flower buds start to develop at the notches of the stems, but remain dormant unless an exceptional drop in temperature triggers them to flower about 25 days later. The edible flowers start to open about 9 p.m., are fully open within 90 minutes and are withered by dawn. However, they can be kept open for longer by chilling in a refrigerator.* × ½ (FJ, v.1, 318)

73▲ 74▼

77 **Malphigia** **coccigera** *(Malphigiaceae)*
"Singapore Holly" *is a small treelet, native to the*
Caribbean. It grows up to 2 m. tall and has small
dark, prickly, shiny leaves like holly, to which it is
not related. Flowers are on orange stalks and
petals are narrow at the bases but broad and
fringed at the tips. Fruits are red and about 8 mm
in diameter. This very neat plant makes handsome
hedges and can be coaxed into a beautiful and
free-flowering dwarf bonsai. × 1 (FM, v.5, 145)

78 **Hibiscus mutabilis** *(Malvaceae).* **Rose of**
Sharon *is a rather ragged shrub from S. China*
with a few thick, upright branches growing up to 4
m. high and bearing large downy leaves. The
corolla changes colour: white when it opens in the
morning, and dark pink when it begins to wither in
the evening. The most usual form grown is the
double-flowered cultivar, illustrated.

× ²/₅ (FJ, v.1, 434)

79 **Hibiscus rosa-sinensis** *(Malvaceae). The*
Red Hibiscus *(Shoe Flower or* Bunga Raya) *is a*
native of S. China, and the National Flower of
Malaysia. It is easily grown from cuttings and
many beautiful cultivars have been developed by
hybridisation. The leaves are used as an emollient
and can be eaten. × 1 (FJ, v.1, 435)

77▲ 78▼

80 Gardenia jasminoides (*G. florida; Rubiaceae*). *A native of S. China, the Gardenia (Bunga Cina) is a 3-m.-high spreading shrub. The double-flowered cultivar, propagated by cuttings, and the form with variegated leaves are common. The flower has a rich "tropical" scent, but it soon turns black in the centre and petals, pale yellow. It is particularly susceptible to mealy bugs. The dried corollas are used to flavour tea.* × ⁵/₆ (FJ, v.2, 313)

81 Ixora javanica (*Rubiaceae*). **Javanese Ixora** (*Pecah Periuk) is a 3-m.-high shrub with showy inflorescences and is native to SE Asia, including Singapore. The paired leaves are moderately pale green, up to 20 cm. long and tend to hang down. Flowers open orange-red, turning red later.*
× ¾ (FJ, v.2, 325)

82 Clerodendrum paniculatum (*Verbenaceae*). **Pagoda Flower** (*Penkilai) is about 3 m. high, slightly branched and woody-based. It is possibly native to SE Asia. Its dark, shiny, 3-lobed leaves have an unpleasant smell, while the characteristic conical flower head comprises numerous small red flowers. Although these appear scentless, they are very attractive to the spectacular Birdwing butterflies. There are several rather similar and beautiful species in the SE Asian region, which should be brought into cultivation.* × ³/₅ (FJ, v.2, 609)

80▲ 81▼

FOLIAGE SHRUBS AND TREELETS

83 **Cordyline terminalis** (C. fruticosa; *Agavaceae*). *The wild* **Ti Plant** *has green leaves, which are used to make leaf skirts in the Pacific as they do not shrivel. The purple-leaved cultivar in the picture is grown for its ornamental foliage. It rarely flowers and old-fashioned Chinese consider its flowering a sign of good luck.* × ¼ (FJ, v.3, 160)

84 **Graptophyllum pictum** (*Acanthaceae*). *Probably a native of E. Indonesia and New Guinea, the* **Caricature Plant** *(Puding) grows to a height of 4 m. Several cultivars are grown, with differently-coloured leaves. Flowers are few, and are always the same colour. It is the host plant of the Autumn Leaf Butterfly,* Doleschallia bisaltide. × ⅔ (FJ, v.2, 579)

85 **Dracaena goldieana** (*Pleomele goldieana; Agavaceae*). **Queen of Dracaenas** *is the most beautiful of all the* Dracaenas, *with its marbled leaves. A native of W. Africa, it is often grown in pots, though it may grow up to 4 m. in the wild. The leaves are rather soft and need protection from direct sunlight, and young leaves are red underneath.* × ¾ (FJ, v.3, 161, 659)

83▲ 84▼

86 Acalypha wilkesiana *(Euphorbiaceae).* ***Jacob's Coat*** *(or Beefsteak Plant) is a shrub up to 3 m. tall, a native of Polynesia, probably Fiji. Several cultivated forms are grown because of their variously coloured leaves; most of these are heart-shaped with pointed tips. Flowers are insignificant and grow on spikes — the female spikes sticking upwards and the male flowers hanging down among the leaves. The young shoots are eaten raw in Java.* × ⅖ (FJ, v.1, 489)

87 Acalypha godseffiana *(Euphorbiaceae). This garden form, possibly of A. wilkesiana, has ruffled leaves due to excessive growth at the side of the leaves when young.* × ⅖

88 Codiaeum variegatum *(Euphorbiaceae).* ***Garden Croton*** *(Puding) is a shrub growing up to about 4 m. high, with a rather upright habit. A native of E. Indonesia and New Guinea, it can be propagated by cutting or from seed, and a large number of cultivars have been produced with remarkable differences in the shape as well as the colour and patterning of the leaves. Reds, yellows and greens predominate. The insignificant male and female flowers occur on separate spikes, but on the same plant. The female flowers have forked stigmas, while the male flowers are pompom-like.*

86▲ 87▼

88

th are typical of wind-pollinated flowers. The
ung shoots can be cooked and eaten.
× ⅖ (FJ, v.1, 493)

Polyscias fruticosa (Nothopanax fruti-
sus; *Araliaceae*). *This small shrub probably
ginated in E. Indonesia. It has an attractive
wth habit, with a few upright but rather
oked branches and fernlike leaves, which are
llowish-green in the cultivar illustrated. It
asionally produces insignificant heads of green-
 flowers, which are just visible at the top left of
 illustration.* × ½ (FJ, v.2, 168)

Schefflera actinophylla (Brassaia actino-
ylla; *Araliaceae*). *The **Octopus** or **Umbrella**
e is a small, sun-loving tree from Queensland
h few upright branches. The large leaves are of
usual shape, having a series of stalked radiating
flets. The central part of the leaf blade, where
 leaflet stalks meet, is webbed rather like the
ric of an umbrella. The name Octopus Tree
nes from the flower spikes, which spread like
 arms of a large upside-down octopus; the
bbed appearance of the fruit looking like an
opus's suckers. Flowers are pink, changing to
, and have copious nectar. Small plants are
en grown in pots.* × ⅟₁₀ (HT, 177)

▲89 ▼90

113

TREES OF THE MANGROVE

91 Rhizophora mucronata *(Rhizophoraceae)*
The **Mangrove Tree** (Bakau Kurap) has sma
greenish-cream flowers that develop to produ
seedlings with pointed root-rudiments up to 60 cm
long. In the picture they are seen hanging from th
branches like javelins. When these fall, they flo
away or stick in the mud and start to grow. Th
species lower down, with narrow leaves and sma
"javelins", is Kandelia candel (Berus-berus),
small tree with buttress roots. The flowers of bot
species can also be seen in the illustration.
× ¹⁄₁₀ (FM, v.5, 45

92 Lumnitzera littorea (L. coccinea; *Combre
taceae*). The beautiful **Red Teruntum** flowe
when quite young. It has shiny, fleshy leaves an
red flowers. It grows on firmer and better-draine
shores than those favoured by most mangro
species.   × ½ (FM, v.4, 58

93 Bruguiera gymnorrhiza *(Rhizophoraceae*
The calyx of the Bruguiera (Tumu Merah)
scarlet, with 12-15 pointed lobes, and the seedlin
has a thick root-rudiment. After sticking in th
mud, a taproot issues from its lower end. It has
buttressed trunk and numerous, many-branche
aerial knee roots.   × ⅔ (FM, v.5, 46

91▲ 92▼

94 ▲

95 ▲ 96 ▼

DRY COAST TREES

94 Barringtonia asiatica (*Lecythidaceae*). **Fish Poison Tree** (Putat Laut or Butun) *is a big spreading tree with large, egg-shaped, dark shiny leaves. It grows wild on sandy and rocky shores though it grows well when planted inland. The large, heavily-scented flowers, with hundreds of showy stamens, open at dusk and are probably pollinated by big moths. Unfortunately petals and stamens drop at dawn. The fruit have a characteristic shape, being about 10 cm. in diameter squarish at the base and tapering towards the tip like a truncated pyramid. They float in the sea and may germinate after drifting great distances. The seeds and other parts of the tree contain saponins and are used as fish poisons.* × ⅓ (TFM, v.2, 258)

95 Terminalia catappa (*Combretaceae*). **Sea Almond** (Ketapang) *is a native of the sandy shores of the Indo-Pacific region, and a favourite tree for roadside plantings. It has a very characteristic pagoda shape. Every few months it sends a single stem shooting up for a distance of about 3 m and growth stops. Then several horizontal branches grow out from the top of the trunk. These have a wavy shape as the end of each branch produces a rosette of leaves, stops growing, then sends a new shoot out from the lower side of the rosette. During dry seasons the leaves turn beautiful colours as they die — red, copper, brown or gold. The seed is an edible nut which is difficult to extract from its flexible, fibrous shell.* (FM, v.4, 548)

96 Calophyllum inophyllum (*Clusiaceae*). **Alexandrine Laurel** (Penaga Laut) *can grow up to a height of 20 m., but it is usually shorter along the seashore. It is commonly planted by roadsides. The shiny dark green leaves have numerous small parallel veins and are very tough. The sweet smelling, short-lasting flowers are followed by poisonous, nearly spherical fruit. The trunk exudes a gum which solidifies, and the seeds contain an oil which was once used for lamps.* × ⅓ (TFM, v.2, 186)

97 Hibiscus tiliaceus (*Malvaceae*). **Sea Hibiscus** (Baru or Baru-baru Laut) *is a small tree with large heart-shaped leaf blades which are downy underneath. The corollas are about 8 cm. in diameter, open at 9 a.m. and change to a pinkish brown before falling the same evening or the next morning. It is very common on all types of seashore and grows wild on dry shores throughout the tropics. Inland from mangrove it indicates the boundary between the upper limit of salt-water penetration and the freshwater swamp. However it grows quite well when planted inland. The bark contains very tough fibres used for cordage and for caulking ships.* × ⅘ (FJ, v.1, 429)

FOREST TREES

98 **Dysoxylum cauliflorum** *(Meliaceae). Th cream-coloured, night-scented flowers of* **Stem Dysoxylum** *are produced on short stems issuing from the tree trunk, and these develop to produce the characteristic orange fruit with black seeds The waxy pulp surrounding the seeds is said to b edible. The trunk has very prominent lenticels.* × 1/4

99 **Cratoxylum formosum** *(Hypericaceae)* **Pink Mempat** *is easily distinguished from the other forest trees when in flower. Once or twice a year, the leaves fall and the flowers are borne among the red-tinged new leaves. Individual flowers open two hours after dawn and close that afternoon. Unfortunately flowering only lasts 2–3 days. As host plant to some butterflies of the genera* Neptis *and* Lasippa, *the tree is sometimes denuded by caterpillars.* × 4/5 (TFM, v.2, 251)

100 **Shorea macroptera** *(Dipterocarpaceae).* Dipterocarp, *in Greek, means "two-winged fruit", however,* Shorea *fruits have 3 large wings, which are enlarged sepals. They cause the fruit to spin when it falls, but as it is rather heavy, it is not blown far by the wind.*

Other Shorea *species include S. curtisii or* Seraya, *easily identified by its bluish, waxy leaves and red, fissured bark (p. 20). The timber of these trees is known as Red Meranti.* × 3/5

98▲ 99▼

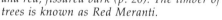

WAYSIDE TREES

101 **Ficus microcarpa** (F. retusa; *Moraceae*)
An extraordinarily versatile tree, the **Malayan Banyan** (Jejawi or Jawi-jawi)'s natural habitats are the river banks and swampy flood plains which lie just inland of the mangrove, and the exposed rocky coasts. It is common in Singapore, where it is often the sole survivor of the original tree flora on the banks of the Singapore River. It is also common on old buildings, where its numerous aerial roots hang down in tasseled festoons, and sometimes develop into thick prop roots. This tree looks like the Benjamin Fig, F. benjamina, but the twigs are thicker and do not droop, the leaves lack drip-tips, and the small fruit do not pass through an orange stage and are purplish-black when they ripen.   × ¹⁄₁₀₀ (TFM, v.3, 151)

102 **Ficus variegata** (*Moraceae*). The **Common Red Stem-fig** grows prolifically in thickets and is capable of reaching quite a large size. The picture shows two of the most characteristic features of trees of the humid tropics — buttresses and cauliflory, the production of flowers from the trunk. The figs also occur on the smaller branches and are green, turning rose red when ripe. Young figs and shoots are eaten raw.   × ¹⁄₃₀ (TFM, v.3, 160)

103 **Caryota mitis** (*Arecaceae*). **Fishtail Palm** (Rabok or Tukas) is the only palm whose leaves are subdivided twice, and whose flower heads, which are in dense bundles, mature from the top of the tree downwards. When fruiting is completed, the stem dies. The fuzz from young leaves was used as tinder and durian sellers line their booths with the leaves. The fruit and the whole plant cause itching when handled because of the presence of minute needle-like crystals found on it. This is the only common native palm in thickets, though the Macarthur's Palm, Ptychospermum macarthurii, (p. 61, right) sows itself freely around colonial bungalows.   (FJ, v.3, 187)

101▲ 102▼

104 **Ficus religiosa** *(Moraceae). A native of India,* **Sacred Bodh Tree** *(or Pipal Tree) is commonly planted in the Asean region, especially by Buddhists, who revere it because it was under one such tree that the Buddha attained enlightenment. A deciduous tree bearing elegant, heart-shaped leaves with a very long drip-tip, it seeds itself freely on masonry, where it behaves as a strangling fig. It produces few aerial roots when growing in soil.*   × ⅓ (FJ, v.2, 33)

105 **Adenanthera pavonina** *(Mimosaceae). Native to SE Asia,* **Coral Tree** *(Saga) is a spreading hardwood up to 30 m. tall. Its small, yellowish flowers grow in dense drooping rat-tail flower heads, almost like catkins. The curved hanging pods, with a bulge opposite each seed, split open each into two twisted halves to reveal the scarlet pill-shaped seeds. These are very hard and can be used as beads. They have also been used since early times in India for weighing gold. The young leaves can be cooked and eaten.*   × ⅓ (FJ, v.1, 563)

106 **Ficus elastica** *(Moraceae). The* **India Rubber Tree** *(Bunoh Seteroh), which grows wild from India to Java, was the principal source of rubber in Asia until early in this century when it was superceded by Para Rubber* (Hevea brasiliensis). *It is a large strangling fig with leathery leaves up to 30 cm. long. The branches are tipped by pointed, red, edible leaf buds, and the tree rarely produces figs. It is very popular as an indoor pot plant in temperate climates.*   (TFM, v.3, 146)

104▲ 105▼

107 **Fagraea fragrans** *(Loganiaceae). The* **Tembusu** *tree is common and probably native in Singapore, where, according to Corner, the finest trees are found. It has characteristic thick, dark, deeply-fissured bark and short, horizontal branches from which issue tall, upright branches bearing small hanging twigs. In May and October, it has clusters of cream-coloured, scented flowers which become yellow when old. The berries, which ripen in September and January, are eaten by fruit bats and birds.*

Another species, F. crenulata, the Cabbage Tree, looks very much like the Sea Almond (p. 116), but has much larger leaves. It is sometimes planted by roadsides.   × ⅙ (FJ, v.2, 211)

108 **Cyrtostachys renda** *(C. lakka; Arecaceae).* **Sealing-wax Palm** *(Pinang Raja) is a native of SE Asian swamp forests, though it grows equally well in dry conditions, reaching a height of about 8 m. The flowers are insignificant and the black fruit are about 1 cm. in diameter. The wood is soft and the roots run a long distance on the surface — a reason they are not planted by the roadsides in towns.*   × ¹⁄₁₀ (FJ, v.3, 192)

109 **Cinnamomum iners** *(Lauraceae). A quick-growing small tree up to about 10 m. high,* **Wild Cinnamon** *(Kayu Manis Hutan or Medang Tejar) puts forth new shoots at frequent intervals. Its small yellowish flowers have an unpleasant waxy smell. The small black fruits are eaten by birds, squirrels and fruit bats, thus dispersing the seeds. The leaves smell faintly of cinnamon and are eaten by caterpillars of the Bluebottle Butterfly,* Graphium sarpedon. × ¼ (FJ, v.1, 120)

110 **Spathodea campanulata** *(Bignoniaceae).* **African Tulip Tree** *is quick-growing, has wind-dispersed seeds and is very common on wasteland. The flower buds are filled with water — natural water-pistols when squeezed — and the bird-pollinated flowers last several days. The canoe-like dry fruit are about 25 cm. long and split lengthwise into two halves. Its shallow roots make it unsuitable for roadside planting.* × ½ (FM, v.8, 185)

111 **Macaranga hypoleuca** (Euphorbiaceae). *This* **Macaranga**, *Mahang Putih, is common in disturbed, well-lit sites. It has blue-green waxy stems and three-lobed leaf blades with hollow, ant-inhabited twigs. It produces tiny, green, wind-pollinated flowers. In the illustration, the ants are feeding on the white food-bodies produced by the plant.* × 1 (FJ, v.1, 488)

109▲ 110▼

ORNAMENTAL FLOWERING TREES

112 Peltophorum pterocarpum (P. inerme Caesalpiniaceae). A native of coastal Malaysia **Yellow Flame** (Batai Laut or Jemerlang) is a small spreading tree with dark green, twice pinnate leaves whose leaflets are often out of alignment. The branched flower heads are born on terminal branches. The young twigs and flower buds are light brown. The chestnut-brown pods colour the whole tree during fruiting season. The hard, yellowish seeds germinate slowly, but can be speeded up by maltreatment. In Java the light grey bark is used to dye batik cloth a dark brown colour.
× ⅕ (FJ, v.1, 547)

113 Cassia bakeriana (Caesalpiniaceae). A native of Thailand, it is one of the 3 species of pink-flowered Cassia occasionally planted in Singapore.

114 Cassia fistula (Caesalpiniaceae). **Indian Laburnum** (Bereksa) is a deciduous tree, native from India to Thailand, with beautiful, long, hanging flower heads. In Singapore it often loses most of its leaves when it flowers. The ripe fruit hang down like lengths of black rubber tubing. The pulp surrounding the seeds is purgative and contains anthraquinones, while the bark is rich in tannins.
× ½ (FJ, v.1, 536)

112▲ 113▼

115 ▲

116 ▲ **117** ▼

115 Delonix regia *(Caesalpiniaceae).* **Flame of the Forest** *(*Sepanggil*) is now common throughout the tropics, though it is almost extinct as a wild tree in its native Madagascar. It is easy to grow from seed and has beautiful pale green, twice-pinnate leaves which turn yellow before dropping. The topmost petal is larger than the others and is a pale whitish-pink colour. The seeds in their flat, hard, sword-like pods rattle when they are shaken. The inner parts of the seeds are eaten in Thailand. In Singapore, the tree is permanently green and flowers infrequently, but in monsoon climates it loses its leaves during the dry season and is completely covered with flowers.*   × ¼ (FJ, v.1, 544)

116 Saraca thaipingensis *(Caesalpiniaceae).* The **Yellow Saraca** *(*Gapis Batang*) is one of the most beautiful trees of the region. Under natural conditions it grows on banks of rocky streams and can stand inundation with the roots trailing in water. However, it grows well when planted on dry ground. The flower clusters emerge from trunk and branches about twice a year after dry weather. What looks like the corolla is the calyx; the flowers have no petals. The young pinnate leaves are produced several times a year. First they hang limply and are mauve; then they turn a light greenish-white before they darken and stiffen. (There is a photograph of the tree in bloom on page 61, left.)*   × ½ (FJ, v.1, 527; v.3, 649)

117 Cerbera odollam *(Apocynaceae).* **Poison Apple** *(*Yellow-eyed Cerbera *or* Pong-pong*) grows wild in the upper part of the mangrove which is only submerged at high tide. Surprisingly it thrives when planted on roadsides. It is small and spreading with neat and shiny leaves, and fruit and flowers to add interest. However, it is poisonous and the irritating sap is said to cause blindness.*

C. manghas is very similar, but the centre of the flowers is pink, not yellow, and it grows wild on dry coasts.   × ⅖ (TFM, v.2, 12)

118 Lagerstroemia speciosa *(L. flos-reginae; Lythraceae).* **Rose of India** *(*Bungor Raya*) is a low tree with spreading branches when planted in open spaces, though it may reach a height of 30 m. in the forest. The oval leaf blades turn red before falling. The flowers are borne on branched flower heads at the end of the branches and are very showy, usually having 6 crinkled petals with narrow stalked bases and many yellow stamens. It is very suitable for roadside planting, and even large branches will take root. Trees only flower occasionally in Singapore.*   × 1 (TFM, v.2, 280)

WILD HERBACEOUS TWINERS

119 **Thunbergia alata** *(Acanthaceae). The small, slender, short-lived* **Black-eyed Susan,** *a native of tropical Africa, was introduced to Singapore about 150 years ago as an ornamental It is now a common wildflower with corollas varying from lemon-yellow to orange, and with or without the "black eye" surrounding the corolla tube.* × ⅔

The rather similar Clock Vine, T. fragrans, has scentless white flowers and is apparently a native of Singapore. It is a more vigorous twiner than T. alata, and it can be seen climbing up fences.

(FJ, v.2 552)

120 **Ipomoea cairica** *(Convolvulaceae). Believed to be of African origin, the* **Railway Creeper** *was probably introduced to Singapore as an ornamental, which has since run wild. It is a very common twiner, growing on hedges and fences, or creeping over the ground where there is no other support. The leaves have 5 radiating lobes of which the outer two may have two lobes. It is often called Morning Glory in Singapore because its flowers open in the morning and are closed by afternoon.* × ⅔ (FM, v.4, 58

119▲

121 **Ipomoea nil** *(Convolvulaceae). This vigorous but short-lived* **Morning Glory** *was probably introduced from tropical America, but has now run wild. The corollas open in the morning and wither in the afternoon.* × ⅓ (FJ, v.2, 494

122 **Lygodium flexuosum** *(Schizaeaceae). The very common* **Climbing Fern** *(Paku Jari) starts life on the ground with fronds whose lobes radiate like the fingers of a hand. It later becomes a slender twiner. Although the twining parts may be several metres long, they are single fronds, there being no true stems above the ground. The spores are produced in special lobes which fringe the spore-bearing leaflets. In the background are the hanging brown aerial roots of a strangling fig (Ficus microcarpa).* × 1 (RFM, v.2, 57

120▲ 121▼

123▲

124▲ 125▼

ORNAMENTAL TWINERS

123 Argyreia nervosa (*Convolvulaceae*). *Elephant Climber is a large, woody twiner native to N. India, where the leaves and roots are used as poultices. It is commonly cultivated and can quickly cover extensive areas with its large velvety leaves. The young shoots and underside of leaves are covered with dense, white silky hairs. The flower buds are enclosed in pale green bracts.*
× ⅓ (FJ, v.2, 497)

124 Thunbergia grandiflora (*Acanthaceae*). *A large, woody twiner, native to India and probably to Singapore, the **Big-flowered Thunbergia** is cultivated for its showy flowers. It is very variable — the corolla may be white, greyish-blue, or a pale, true blue, and there are hairy and hairless forms. The flowers are often visited by the large female Carpenter Bees.*
× ½ (FJ, v.2, 552)

125 Allamanda cathartica (*Apocynaceae*). *The **Yellow Allamanda** is a native of NE S. America and adjacent parts of Central America, where it grows on river banks as a large woody twiner. There is a large-flowered var. grandiflora which has a corolla 10 cm. in diameter. Recently, dwarf shrubby cultivars have been developed. The spiny fruit looks like a small durian. The plant is purgative and contains a poisonous latex. It often continues to grow at the sites of earlier habitations.*
× ⅓ (FJ, v.2, 223)

126 Clitorea ternatea (*Papilionaceae*). *Though named after Ternate in the Spice Islands, the **Butterfly Pea** (Upside-down Pea or Kacang Telang) is probably of S. American origin. It is a slender perennial twiner growing to about 3 m. high. The short flower stem is bent backwards so that the largest petal is underneath, unlike most members of the Pea-flower family, and it provides a platform for large insects like Carpenter Bees. The anthocyanin pigment in the petals is used to colour nonya cakes blue.*
× 2 (FJ, v.1, 623)

127 (following pages) **Mucuna bennettii** (*Papilionaceae*). *The large **New Guinea Climber** was grown from seeds collected in New Guinea by Fred Shaw Mayer, who thought they belonged to a blue-flowered Mucuna whose petals were lying on the forest floor near by. It was grown by Dr. Holttum at the Singapore Botanic Gardens, who must have been thrilled when one of the world's most spectacular twiners burst into flower. The calyx is covered with fine, stiff hairs, which penetrate the skin and cause itching.*
× ¾

TENDRIL CLIMBERS AND SCRAMBLERS

128 Nepenthes rafflesiana (Nepenthaceae) Pitcher plants (Periuk Kera) start off as rosette plants and later climb by tendrils. Each leaf has a tendril at the apex which may bear a pitcher at its tip. The pitchers are nearly half-full of liquid which contains a protein-digestive enzyme, and have lids, on the underside of which are nectar glands that attract insects. The mouths of the pitchers have smooth rims which offer no footholds, thus they are very efficient traps for insects which provide the plants with some of their nitrogen needs. This is important as pitcher plants, like most carnivorous plants, grow on poor, acid soils, which tend to be deficient in nitrogen. The illustration shows a male **Raffles' Pitcher Plant** in flower, and a pitcher of the smaller N. gracilis can be seen in the background. × ¼

129 Passiflora foetida (Passifloraceae). **Stinking Passionflower** (Timun Dendang), a little, pan-tropical herbaceous tendril climber, came from S. America. The whole plant has an unpleasant smell. The flower bud and unripe fruit are enclosed in a basket formed from 3 finely subdivided bracts bearing sticky glandular hairs. The shoots can be cooked and eaten, and the pulp of the small, yellow berries is deliciously sweet. The fruit

128▲ 129▼

end to ripen at the same time, and birds (and children) like to eat them. × ⅘ (FJ, v.1, 290)

130 Bougainvillea hybrid *(Nyctaginaceae). Bougainvilleas (Bunga Kertas) are large, woody scramblers which climb with the aid of thorny branchlets in their native forests in tropical S. America. The cultivated forms are probably hybrids of* B. spectabilis, B. glabra *and* B. peruviana, *but their precise ancestry is unknown. In Singapore they are usually cultivated as pot plants or trimmed bushes, and they flower most freely when kept short of water and root space. Their colourful show is due to groups of 3 thin bracts, in the centre of which are 2–3 small tubular flowers.*
× ⅖ (FJ, v.1, 271)

131 Saritaea magnifica *(Bignonia magnifica; Bignoniaceae). A tendril climber which is a native of Columbia, this* Saritaea *(or* Bignonia) *is probably the best of several related ornamental climbers, such as the Garlic Vine,* Pseudocalymma alliaceum, *of Guatemala, whose occasional flowering is too brief.* Saritaea's *flowers are short-lasting, but it produces flushes of flowers every few days. It will grow vigorously up trees and bushes but, as it has a straggly growth habit, it does not shade its host plant sufficiently to do it much damage.* × 1 (FM, v.8, 184)

▲130 ▼131

NON-FLOWERING EPIPHYTES

132   Platycerium coronarium *(Polypodiaceae).* *The giant* **Antler** *or* **Staghorn Fern** *(Semun Bidadari) is commonest on big trees in the Catchment Area, but is not very plentiful. It occasionally grows on rubber trees, as the illustration shows. The nest-fronds have lobed upper parts and rounded lower ends which persist and eventually surround a large globular mass of organic debris. It also has antler-like hanging branched leaves over 2 m. long. These carry large, kidney-shaped fertile lobes which have the spore-bearing organs on their concave undersides amidst a dense mat of brown hairs.* × ¹⁄₂₀ (RFM, v.2, 138)

133   *Oil palms produce ideal conditions for epiphytic ferns. The central trunk has* Davallia denticulata, *or Rabbit's Foot Fern, which has a thick, black-haired creeping stem and lacy, leathery leaflets. It is used as greenery by florists.* (RFM, v.2, 359) *The trunk on the left bears young* Asplenium nidus, *or Bird's Nest Fern.*
× ¹⁄₁₅ (RFM, v.2, 419)

134   Polyporus *sp.* *(Polyporaceae).* **Bracket Fungus** *plays an important role in the decomposition of dead wood, though some fungi which start to grow on dead wood in wounds of trees may later damage living tissues. The feeding part of the plant consists of fine threads which penetrate the dead wood. The visible bracket is the reproductive part, on the underside of which are minute spore-producing cells. The illustration shows 3 species of Fungus Beetle,* **Eumorphus,** *and their larvae feeding on the spores.* × ²⁄₃

135   Phymatodes sinuosa (Polypodium sinuosum; *Polypodiaceae). The thick, hollow creeping stems of this* **Ant Fern** *are covered by scales and are often inhabited by ants. The simple, elongated fronds bear two rows of large brown patches which are the spore-producing organs.*
× 1 (RFM, v.2, 190)

132▲ 133▼

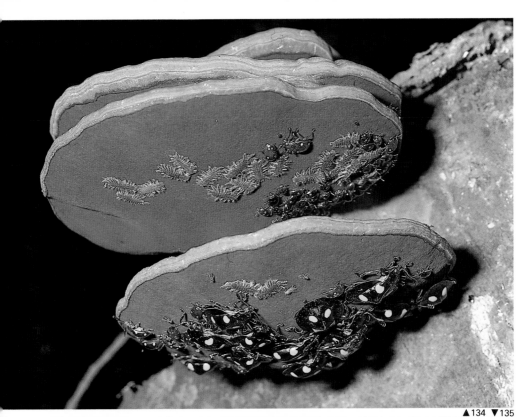

▲134 ▼135

FLOWERING EPIPHYTES

136 Dendrobium anosmum (D. superbum, Orchidaceae). *The epithet* anosmum, *Greek for "scentless", is a misnomer for the flowers smell, to me, like raspberry jam, but with a slightly pungent quality reminiscent of iron filings. A SE Asian native, the biggest-flowered* Dendrobiums *are from the Philippines. It flowers profusely every few months from bare stems, but the flowers do not last long. This beautiful orchid is now considered "old-fashioned".* × ⅖ (FJ, v.3, 374)

137 Dendrobium crumenatum (*Orchidaceae*). *The commonest flowering plant epiphytic in Singapore,* **Pigeon Orchid** (Anggerek Merpati) *forms large clumps on roadside trees. Stems have a spindle-shaped, swollen pseudo-bulb near the base, a long mid-section bearing leaves and, sometimes, a slender, knotted, flowering part at the tip. Flower buds remain dormant until stimulated to develop by a large fall in temperature due to a rainstorm. Flowering is 9 days later for a few hours only. Hence nearly all the pigeon orchids in Singapore bloom on the same day, several times a year. The morning after, the closed flowers look like upside-down white pigeons. These flowers are delightfully fragrant. Unlike most orchid species in the region, the pigeon orchid does not hybridise easily.* × ⅙ (RFM, v.1, 8, 14, 17, 329)

138 Bulbophyllum vaginatum (*Orchidaceae*) *This Bulbophyllum is a common epiphyte with creeping rootstocks bearing occasional pseudo-bulbs, each with a broad dark green leaf. It often forms dense mats over a considerable area of the trunks of old trees such as* Eugenia grandis, *which can be found along Cluny Road and the northern end of Holland Road. It flowers gregariously, and each flower head has about 15 small flowers, each with two greatly elongated sepals.* × 1 (FJ, v.3, 381)

136▲ 137▼

FRUITS

139 Nephelium lappaceum *(Sapindaceae).* **Rambutan** *trees produce flushes of leaves and small, yellowish-green flowers twice a year, and fruits ripen around July and December. Usually a tree has one large crop and one small crop of fruit. The fruit hang down in bunches and may colour the whole tree red or yellow. The edible, white, translucent flesh is attached to the single central seed in the wild type, but is free and sweet in cultivars. Fruit skins, leaves, bark and roots are used in traditional medicine. It is the host plant of the Red Flash Butterfly,* Rapala iarbus.

× ⅓ (FJ, v.2, 138)

140 Durio zibethinus *(Bombacaceae). I boggle at the task of writing about the* **Durian** *in so few words. Some Singaporeans relish it so much that they make the thousand-kilometre journey to S Thailand during the season; yet others, starting with Stamford Raffles, abominate it. The bat-pollinated, edible flowers hang from the branches and produce the fruit at the middle and end of the year. This should be eaten only after it falls from the tree. The fruit is the perfect packing job — earth may tremble when it hits the ground, yet the soft creamy flesh stays intact. The seeds only stand drying for 1–2 days before losing viability. The illustration shows an unusual situation — a fruit and flower buds at the same time.*

× 1/12 (TFM, v.1, 113)

141 Manilkara achras *(Achras zapota; Sapotaceae). A native of Central America, where it is a tall forest tree,* **Chicle** *(Sapodilla or Chiku) latex is the principal source of chewing-gum base. Introduced to Manila by the Spaniards, we know it as a low, spreading fruit tree. The small, white, fragrant flowers open at night. The fruit has juicy brown flesh with a distinctive flavour and elongated, shiny black seeds.* × ⅘ (FJ, v.2, 191)

142 Ananas comosus *(A. sativus; Bromeliaceae). All members of the Pineapple family are natives of tropical America. The* **Pineapple** *(Nanas) plant's stiff leaves have saw-toothed edges. The main stem carries a compressed flower head at its apex (as shown in the picture). The individual fruits fuse with their neighbours to become the familiar pineapple. The fruit has a stinging after-effect on the mouth due to the protein-digesting enzyme, bromelin. Cooking slices of meat with pineapple softens it. The barong tagalog, the Filipino dress shirt, is made from the strong, but delicate, pineapple fibre. Ornamental varieties with yellow- or pink-edged leaves are grown.* × 1 (TCM, 76)

139▲ 140▼

143 **Carica papaya** *(Caricaceae). A native of Mexico,* **Papaya** *(Pawpaw or Betek) is a giant herb, not a true tree, as the stem contains only a basketwork of fibres set in soft pulp. It is easy to grow in a confined space, but needs well-drained soil, otherwise the base of the stem will rot. Within 6 months of planting it can bear fruit which are rich in beta carotene and ascorbic acid (Provitamin A and Vitamin C). The fruit are usually picked as soon as they begin to turn yellow, or the birds will get them. The plants may produce large female flowers, which usually need no pollination, or small male or bisexual flowers. The whole plant — except for the ripe fruit — contains a latex whose principal solid component is the enzyme papain which converts proteins to their constituent amino acids. This is used to tenderise meat and for various medical and industrial purposes.*

× ¹⁄₂₀ (FJ, v.1, 314)

144 **Lansium domesticum** *(Meliaceae). A medium-sized native tree with fluted trunk and pinnate leaves,* **Langsat** *has delicious fruit. However, the thin skin of the fruit contains latex, and the large seeds embedded in the flesh are very bitter.*

Duku is included in the same species as langsat because intermediate forms exist, but it can be easily distinguished because of its smaller clusters of larger, darker fruits (up to 5 cm. in diameter, without adherent sepals. Also, its thick skin does not contain latex. × ¹⁄₈ (FJ, v.2, 125)

145 **Mangifera indica** *(Anacardiaceae). Several species of* Mangifera *native to the region's forests are grown in Singapore, but the best known of these is the* **Mango** *(Mangga), which is probably a native of monsoon India. It is rather straggly when young, but matures to a splendid tall tree with a dense, hemispherical crown. Although the climate is not well suited for it and it is often at the mercy of wood-boring beetle larvae, this tree is popular in suburban gardens. It flowers after a dry period, but though it is common for parts of the tree to put out new leaves, it is rare for it to fruit and flower simultaneously.*

Other species grown in Singapore are Binjai *(M. caesia) and the strong-smelling* Macang *(M. foetida).* × ¹⁄₆ (FM, v.8, 427)

143▲ 144▼

146 **Eugenia malaccensis** (Syzygium malaccense; *Myrtaceae*). *Malay Apple (Pomerack or Jambu Merah) is a narrow tree, up to about 15 m in height, cultivated throughout the region. The leaves are often covered in galls containing larvae of psyllid bugs. It flowers and fruits several times a year. The fruits are whitish green, red or red-streaked, and contain a single large seed. The skin is delicate, so it is not sold in the market.*

× ⅖ (TFM, v.3, 247)

147 **Eugenia aquea** (Syzygium aqueum; *Myrtaceae*). *Water Apple (Jambu Air) is a small spreading tree up to 10 m. high, probably of Indian origin. The creamy white flowers have large numbers of showy stamens. The pear-shaped fruit have thin skins and translucent flesh, so appear waxy. Flowers and fruit are beautiful, but the crispy white flesh is rather tasteless.* × ¼ (FJ, v.3, 247)

148 **Passiflora laurifolia** (*Passifloraceae*). *A slender, woody, S. American passionfruit vine which climbs by tendrils, Water Lemon (Buah Susu) is common in belukar, but it fruits more freely when grown in full sunlight. Flowers are fragrant and close in the afternoon. The fruit resembles a smooth lemon, but has delicious watery pulp. The laurel-like leaves are said to be poisonous.* × 1 (FJ, v.1, 290)

146▲ 147▼

149▲ 150▼

FRUIT VEGETABLES

149 Vigna sesquipedalis (V. sinensis *var.* sesquipedalis; *Papilionaceae*). *A tall twiner usually grown on poles by market-gardeners, the* **Long Bean** (Kacang Panjang) *has rather dull-coloured whitish, yellowish or bluish flowers. The pods are cylindrical and nearly 1 cm. in diameter and 30–100 cm. in length, with a rough surface. The unripe pods are cooked as a vegetable. The young leaves are eaten boiled or steamed in Java.*
× ⅕ (TCD, 322)

150 Hibiscus esculentus (Abelmoschus esculentus; *Malvaceae*). *Originally from tropical Africa,* **Okra** (Lady's Finger or Kacang Bendi) *is a robust, short-lived herb growing up to 2 m. tall. It is usually cultivated for the unripe fruits, which are cooked as a vegetable. They contain a mucilage which has several industrial and medicinal uses, including that of a blood volume expander for intravenous administration.* × ¼ (FJ, v.1, 435)

151 Artocarpus altilis (A. incisa; *Moraceae*). **Breadfruit** (Sukun) *is a native of Polynesia, and it may be a hybrid; and, as the tree from which "bread itself is gathered as a fruit", it impressed many Europeans. This is why the vessel H.M.S. Bounty was in the Pacific in 1789 — especially to transport breadfruit seedlings to the Caribbean — when the mutiny occurred. The compound fruit is up to 30 cm. long, nearly spherical and contains up to 20% of starch by weight. It is delicious cut into slices and fried. It is propagated by root cuttings, but this tree and its fruit seem to be out of fashion. In the illustration, the male flower head can be seen sticking upward.*

Other members of this genus often grown in Singapore are the Jackfruit (Nangka, A. heterophyllus), which has enormous compound fruit measuring up to 80 × 30 cm. and the smaller Chempedak (A. integer). The flesh surrounding the seed, which is derived from the stamens, is eaten raw, and the seeds and unripe fruit can be eaten cooked. The seeds of the Jackfruit contain a high concentration of the neurotransmitter acetyl choline, which is destroyed in the gut when the seeds are eaten. × ⅓ (FJ, v.2, 18)

152 Solanum melongena (*Solanaceae*). **Eggplant** (Brinjal or Terung) *was domesticated in India, where it grows wild, and it may reach a height of 1.5 m. It is usually grown as an annual, though it is a perennial. The fruit vary considerably: some cultivars have white fruit, and the shape ranges from spherical to elongated.*
× ⅓ (FJ, v.2, 474)

▲151 ▼152

LEAF AND ROOT VEGETABLES

153 Sauropus androgynus *(Euphorbiaceae).* **Cekup Manis** *is a rather soft-stemmed shrublet or treelet with a few green upright stems and drooping side-branches which occasionally bear hanging 3-chambered fruit. It grows wild in Peninsular Malaysia and is easily grown from cuttings. Young branches are sold in the markets; the leaves are stripped off and boiled or eaten raw. They have a rather strong and distinctive flavour and are exceptionally nutritious. They contain the alkaloid papaverine, but in harmless quantities.*
× ½ (FJ, v.1, 471)

154 Brassica cultivar *(probably* B. para-chinensis, B. chinensis *var.* parachinensis; *Brassicaceae).* **Choy Sum** (Chye Sim) *is one of the most popular leafy vegetables and is often grown on local farms. It has narrow green leafstalks and a slightly bitter taste when eaten raw. It is easily distinguished from the locally-grown* Pak Choy (B. chinensis), *which has broad, white leafstalks and darker green leaves.* × ½

155 Ipomoea aquatica *(*I. reptans; *Convolvulus).* **Water Convolvulus** (Kangkong) *is common throughout the region, both wild and cultivated. It has hollow, floating stems, which may take root in the mud. The form often cultivated in Singapore grows on dry land. It differs from the water form in that it is grown from seeds, not cuttings. Some forms have white corollas. Leaves and stems are cooked as a vegetable, and it is used as pig and fish food. The raw leaves are mildly laxative, and are a rich source of iron.*

One other important Ipomoea *is the Sweet Potato or* Keledek (I. batatas) *from S. America. It has apparently been in the region for a long time, and is the staple food of the New Guinea highlanders.* × ⅗ (FJ, v.2, 496)

156 Xanthosoma sagittifolium *(Araceae).* **Cocoyam** (Keladi Sarawak) *is of American origin, but there is a very similar native taro,* Colocasia esculenta (C. antiquorum) (Keladi Telur, Keladi Cina). *Both grow in moist places and have edible tubers. The native taro can be distinguished from cocoyam by its leaf stems which join the underside of the leaf blade while those of the cocoyam join at the margin of the leaf blade.* × ¹/₁₀ (TCM, 70)

153▲ 154▼

▲155 ▼156

157▲ 158▼

SPICES AND FLAVOURINGS

157 Averrhoa bilimbi *(Oxalidaceae). The flowers of* **Belimbing Asam** *are borne on older branches and on the main trunk. The fruit are very acid and are used, cooked or raw, in the place of vinegar. They are useful for removing stains on fabric and metal. The pale green downy leaves have two rows of sensitive leaflets that droop slowly when shaken briskly. This tree is probably of SE Asian origin. Charles Darwin grew it in his greenhouse and used it in his studies on motion in plants.* × ½ (FT, v.2, 22)

158 Nicolaia elatior *(Phaeomeria speciosa; Zingiberaceae).* **Torch Ginger** *(Kantan) is a native of Indonesia and Malaysia. It has stems up to 6 m. high of typical ginger growth habit. The pyramidal flower heads are shown in the photograph, and they grow on naked flowering stems about 1 m. high. The flower buds are protected by bracts and the small red tubular flowers with orange margins are exposed as the bracts open outwards. The outermost bracts are by far the largest. The flower head in the "drumstick" stage (before the flowers are exposed) is sliced and eaten raw in the Malay dish,* rojak. × ⅖ (FJ, v.3, 64)

159 Myristica fragrans *(Myristicaceae).* **Nutmeg** *(Pala) is a native of the Moluccas (or Spice Islands) in E. Indonesia. A small tree, it was cultivated by Raffles, but is now rare in Singapore. The fruit contains a single seed, the nutmeg, surrounded by an incomplete red aril, which is the spice mace. The whole is encased in a fleshy husk, not used in international commerce, which is delicious when candied. Nutmeg is very poisonous and hallucinogenic, but not in the minute quantities normally eaten. The illustration shows one of the fruit cut into half, thus exposing the mace and nutmeg.* × ½ (TCD, 391)

160 Capsicum frutescens *var.* **minimum** *(Solanaceae).* Capsicums *are one of the ancient foods of tropical America brought back to Spain by Colombus. The cultivars are either the annuals,* C. annuum, *or the shrubby perennials,* C. frutescens, *itself with varieties ranging from the large, fleshy but mild Green Pepper, var.* grossum, *to the tiny and fiery* **Bird Chillies** *(Chili Padi) shown in the photograph. The seeds of all varieties have a burning taste due to minute quantities of capsicain, used in medicine as a counter-irritant. Ascorbic acid was first isolated by the Hungarian biochemist, Szent-Gyorgyi, from* paprika. × ⅕ (TCD, 526)

▲159 ▼160

SOME USEFUL TREES

161 Ceiba pentandra *(Bombacaceae).* **Kapo** *(or Kekabu) has green-barked, horizontal bran ches which come off the straight, blunt-spined grey trunk in groups. The deciduous leaves hav many radiating leaflets, while the off-white, ba pollinated flowers smell of sour milk. The wind borne seeds are supported by air-filled fibres whic repel water and are used for stuffing and fo insulation. Unripe fruit and the seed oil are edible It is an important crop in Java.* × ¹/₁₀ (FJ, v.1, 41

162 Cocos nucifera *(Arecaceae). The origin home of the very useful* **Coconut** *(Kelapa Nyor) is a mystery. Its closest relatives are American; yet it apparently only grew on Pan ma's Pacific coast before Columbus' time.*

Here, the flower spikes bearing two female an numerous male flowers are shown. × ¹/₆ (TCM, 44C

163 Areca catecu *(Arecaceae). The* **Areca Paln** *(Pokok Pinang) is a tall, slender, single-stemme palm grown for its nut-like seeds which contai arecoline. The nut is strongly astringent an contains up to 25% of catechol tannins. It is th "nut" in the betel-nut quid and is very hard. grinds down the teeth, thus it provides som protection against tooth decay.* × ¹/₁₀ (FJ, v.3, 194

161▲ 162▼

154

GLOSSARY

aril: An appendage or outer covering of a seed, often fleshy (e.g. in rambutan and durian).

Aroid: A member of the Arum family (Araceae).

axil: The upper angle between stem and leaf, a common site of origin of buds or roots.

berry: A juicy fruit with numerous seeds embedded in pulp.

bract: A leaf-like structure below a flower or flower head.

bulb: A much shortened stem bearing fleshy leaf bases or scale leaves (e.g. onion).

calyx: The outer envelope of a flower, consisting of separate sepals or fused calyx-lobes, typically green.

corolla: The inner envelope of a flower, consisting of separate petals or fused corolla-lobes, typically not green.

cultivar: (abbr. cv.) A variety of plant which originated in cultivation and maintains its characteristics when propagated.

Dipterocarp: A member of the family Dipterocarpaceae; the most important of the timber trees in South-east Asia.

double-flowered: A flower with an increased number of petals; often the other floral parts are underdeveloped.

herb: A plant with a soft, non-woody stem (herbaceous plant).

hybrid: The progeny of parents of different genetic constitutions.

latex: A milky juice, often containing rubber, found in certain plants.

leaflet: The individual parts of a compound leaf.

node: A joint in a stem from which leaves usually arise.

petal: One of the inner series of sterile leaf-like organs of a flower, usually not green; a constituent part of the corolla.

pinnate leaf: A compound leaf divided once, twice or thrice into leaflets.

pistil: The female part of a flower, consisting of the ovary at the base, and the (sometimes) elongated style tipped by the stigma.

rhizome: An underground stem bearing buds (e.g. in ginger).

sepal: One of the outer series of sterile leaf-like organs of a flower, usually green; a constituent part of the calyx.

shrub: A woody plant which branches at ground level, typically with more than one stem.

sp.: (plural spp.) Abbreviation for species, used after the generic name when the specific name is not given.

spathe: A large bract enclosing a flower head (e.g. in Aroids and Palms).

spike: A flower head bearing stalkless flowers on a single axis.

ssp.: Abbreviation for subspecies.

stamen: The male reproductive organ of a flower, consisting of the (usually yellow) anther which produces pollen grains, and the threadlike filament which supports it.

tree: A large woody plant with a single main stem.

treelet: A small tree.

variety: (abbr. var.) A naturally occuring subdivision of a species.

BIBLIOGRAPHY

Floras: *These scholarly books aim to deal with all members of certain plant groups growing in a defined area.*

Flora of Java, 3 vols., C.A. Backer and Bakhuizen van den Brink, R.C. (1963–8) Noordhoff, Groningen. 2140 pp. Describes most wild and cultivated plants which grow in Singapore.

Flora Malesiana, ed. C.G.G.J. van Steenis, various authors. Series 1, Flowering plants, v.1 (1950) – v.9 (1983). The definitive flora (partly completed) of the region encompassing Brunei, Indonesia, Malaysia, Singapore and New Guinea. Some species illustrated by line drawings.

Flora of Thailand, eds. Tem Smetinand and Kai Larsen, numerous authors. Until v.3 (1979) ASRT Press, Bangkok. A definitive flora, of which only a small part has been completed. Partly illustrated by line drawings.

A Revised Flora of Malaya, 3 vols.: v.1 Orchids, R.E. Holttum — 2nd ed. (1973), v.2 Ferns, R.E. Holttum — 2nd ed. (1968), v.3 Grasses, H.B. Gilliland (1971) Government Printing Office, Singapore. Covers the species found in the Malay Peninsula and Singapore. Partly illustrated.

Tree Flora of Malaya, vols. 1–2, ed. T.C. Whitmore, vol. 3, ed. F.S.P. Ng (1972–) Longman, Kuala Lumpur and London. A forest flora of native trees, to be completed by volume 4.

Other references:

Hortus Third (1976) Macmillan, New York. 1290 pp. A concise dictionary of plants cultivated in the United States and Canada, with descriptions of over 20,000 species and many cultivars.

Allen, B.M., *Malayan Fruits* (1967) Donald Moore Press, Singapore. 246 pp.

Corner, E.J.H., *Wayside Trees of Malaya*, 2 vols., 2nd ed. (1952) Government Printer, Singapore. 1004 pp.

Foo Tok Shiew, *A Guide to the Wildflowers of Singapore* (1985) Singapore Science Centre. 160 pp. A description of 82 plants, mostly common weedy herbs, not found in this book. Fully illustrated with colour photographs and line drawings.

Henderson, M.R., *Malayan Wildflowers*, 2 vols. (1954) Malayan Nature Society, Kuala Lumpur. 835 pp.

Henderson, M.R., *Common Malayan Wildflowers* (1961) Longmans Malayan Nature Series. 69 pp.

Holttum, R.E., *Plant Life in Malaya*, 1st paperback ed. (1977) Longman Malaysia. 254 pp.

Johnson, Anne, *The Ferns of Singapore Island*, 2nd ed. (1977) Singapore University Press. 126 pp.

Keng, H. "Annotated list of seed plants of Singapore" (1973–) Part 1 in vol. 26, pp. 233–7 *Gardens Bulletin*, Singapore. Ten parts published to date.

Pursglove, J.W., *Tropical Crops Dicotyledons* (1974) Longman. 719 pp. *Tropical Crops Monocotyledons* (1975) Longman. 607 pp. Together they form an authoritative account of tropical crops by the 1954–7 Director of the Singapore Botanical Gardens.

Teo Lee Wei and Wee Yeow Chin, *Seaweeds of Singapore* (1983) Singapore University Press. 123 pp.

Whitmore, T.C., *Tropical Rain Forests of the Far East* (1975) Clarendon Press, Oxford. 281 pp.

Whitmore, T.C., *Palms of Malaya*, revised ed. (1977) Oxford University Press, Kuala Lumpur and Singapore. 132 pp.

Wee Yeow Chin, *A Guide to the Ferns of Singapore* (1983) Singapore Science Centre. 72 pp.

INDEX OF SCIENTIFIC NAMES OF PLANTS

* Species illustrated on this page

ACKNOWLEDGEMENTS

It is a pleasure to acknowledge the help of friends. While they have certainly helped in many ways to make this a better book, they cannot be held responsible for any errors and shortcomings which may exist.

I would like to thank in particular:

Mr James Maxwell of Chiangmai University, Thailand and *Dr Benjamin Stone* of the Academy of Natural Sciences, Philadelphia, U.S.A. for reading through the text and offering much valuable advice.

Dr. Chang Kiaw Lan, Haji Mohd. Shah and *Dr. Tan Wee Kiat* of the Singapore Botanic Gardens, and *Dr. Richard Corlett, Dr. Hsuan Keng* and *Dr. Wee Yeow Chin* of the National University of Singapore for the help they have given in establishing the identity of the plants illustrated.

Amy and John Ede of Singapore Orchids Private Limited for providing the facilities for the taking of the photographs on page 19.

PHOTO CREDITS

All photographs in this book by *Ivan Polunin* with the exception of the following:

George Hall   p. 34

Jimmy Kang   p. 130 (No. 120)

Kwan Hun   pp. 27, 44, 67 (No. 7), 88 (No. 45), 98 (No. 62), 106 (No. 77), 109, 130 (No. 119), 138 (No. 132) and 143 (No. 142)

Lawrence Lim   pp. 2, 6, 13, 14, 38, 41, 46, 50, 52, 56, 58, 61, 66 (No. 5), 68 (No. 9), 69, 76 (No. 21), 77 (No. 22), 78 (No. 25), 85, 86 (No. 41), 88 (No. 44), 89, 93 (Nos. 50 & 52), 98 (No. 61), 108 (No. 80), 111, 120 (No. 101), 121, 123 (No. 108), 127, 132 (No. 123), 142 (No. 140), 145, 149 (No. 151), 150 (No. 154) and 155

Leo Meier/Weldon Trannies   p. 20

Shaharin Yussof   p. 132 (No. 124)